175 Home Plans
Multi-Level & Two Story
Designs by William G. Chirgotis, Architect

Creative Homeowner Press

Contents

Complete Index of Homes can be found on page 7

WHY AN ARCHITECT-DESIGNED HOME?

Because an architect is seldom consulted by the average family, his is a little-understood profession. Most people think of an architect as man who designs skyscrapers, factories, churches, schools, and other massive structures which make up a crowded community. Few realize that the majority of architects contribute their talents to solving today's rural and suburban residential problems—the problems which the average family face when they plan to have a new home. So few families realize this fact that less than 5% of them start their planning by visiting an architect. The other 95% visit a model home built in a development or perhaps buy blueprints from a stock plan service. Either way, they may still be receiving indirectly the benefit of architectural talent, if the model or the stock plan represents the work of an architect. A house designed by an architect will certainly give the potential homeowner a correct layout, proper design, and good dollar value.

If you intend to use stock plans to construct your home, be sure that they are the work of a reputable architect. By making the blueprints of these homes available at a small fraction of their original cost to prepare, thousands of families who build from our plans enjoy a better standard of living. Avoid plans which bear the name of a designer but not an architect. The largest investment of your lifetime deserves the insurance of an architect's name indicating the authenticity of the design.

In many sections of the country, there are no architects for miles around. Even in outlying sections of major cities, architects are often too busy to be available for small home work. If this is the case,

you will undoubtedly consider purchasing a stock plan. A stock plan is a home design which is already in the form of working drawings. By permitting the resulting home design to be published, the architect makes the plan available to other families with similar requirements, and it costs them only a fraction of the original cost. They receive copies of substantially the identical blueprints from which the house was constructed, perhaps with some improvements and refinements gained from experience in building it. If you do employ an architect, one or more stock plans can serve as a starting point for your discussions, serving to crystallize your ideas and accelerate the planning. If the plan you buy is architect-designed, you can be certain that when it is properly executed by a competent builder, you are going to be the proud owner of a home which is solidly built, space-engineered, comfort-endowed, and esthetically appealing. In short, you insure your investment by getting the maximum house per dollar spent. The homes illustrated in this book have layouts suited to a great segment of families all over the country and in popular income brackets. As you leaf through the portfolios which follow, you will see many homes that you feel you have seen and admired before. It is quite likely that you have driven past them and envied their lucky owners. They all exist. They are now available to you.

It is the aim of this book to display the home designs of one of this country's leading architects, William G. Chirgotis, to make these homes available to the home-building public, and to point out how architectural services can help any family to attain a home which meets their highest aspirations.

A Guide to Assist You in Selecting a Home Design to Fit Your Needs!

Of the many homes illustrated in this plan book, one is certain to be your "Dream Home" meeting your budget and family requirements. The question is: which one?

The answer, of course, depends on a number of factors. Some are purely personal considerations of taste. Others are basic family needs. Still others are financial. It will be necessary for you to analyze each design on all counts. Here are some of the important points to keep in mind.

Number of Rooms:

Requirements depend on the size of the family. If financially feasible, it is a good idea to provide separate bedrooms for each child and at least two bathrooms if there is more than one child. If there is a "third generation"—for example, a grandparent—a separate bedroom with private bath is virtually essential.

Style:

Colonial or contemporary? This question depends largely on personal preference or taste. It is unwise to build a home which is radically "different" from the other homes in the neighborhood.

Type:

Each basic house type has its own definite advantages. The one-story ranch allows for easy living and maintenance. The two-story and 1½ story Cape Cod offer low cost per square foot, also the complete separation of entertainment and sleeping areas. The split-level and multi-level combine the best features of both types.

Multi-Level

Sometimes called by other names, such as Hi-ranch and Bi-level. In this type of house, the front foyer is at ground level, with a stairway up to the main living area and another down to what would ordinarily be the basement. Because the basement is raised out of the ground enough to permit windows above ground, the area is utilized for living purposes and usually contains a recreation or informal room.

Split-Level

This type features three or four levels. It offers separation of living and bedroom areas, as in a two-story house, but the flights of stairs are shorter. Split-levels are especially suitable for rolling terrain. More land is required than for a two-story, but more livable space is possible on the same land than in a ranch.

Two-Story

Cost, on the basis of amount per square foot, is usually lower than other types of houses. The upstairs bedrooms have more privacy. The two-story should have at least one bath on each floor. More rooms can be built on less land than with any other type.

Expansion Ranch

The expansion ranch is sometimes called a 1½-story house. The half-a-story usually refers to an attic which can be finished at the time of the original construction or later on. This plan often features a master bedroom on the first floor, with children's bedrooms upstairs. Most 1½-story houses have traditional details in the Cape Cod style.

Dome Homes

Introduced about twenty years ago, this unique concept of living is today enjoying phenomenal popularity.

Technically, the dome home originated from the sphere, nature's most favored and efficient means of enclosing unobstructed floor space economically.

Due to inflation and the continued ever-increasing building construction costs and the fact that the factory-assembled, triangular space frames are simply bolted together on the site to form the finished building, drastic reductions are possible on quantities of building materials and on-site labor costs. A dome home can cost as much as 20 percent less than conventional housing.

The dome provides a living area which also answers the need for efficient energy consumption; the dome home is particularly adaptable to solar heating.

Today's dome homes are attractive and offer an exciting new way of living. The minute you step inside the front entrance, you are surrounded by fascinating forms and deceptively large spaces.

Because air naturally travels in a circular pattern, heating and/or cooling a dome home is more efficient and economical.

The dome provides maximum enclosed space with minimum surface area, which means efficiency in terms of heat-gain or heat-loss. It has been estimated that heating, cooling, and insurance costs can be reduced by at least 30 percent.

Americans are shedding the conservative trappings of their urban life and are adapting a more youthful, modern, and exciting life style.

How to Read a Floor Plan

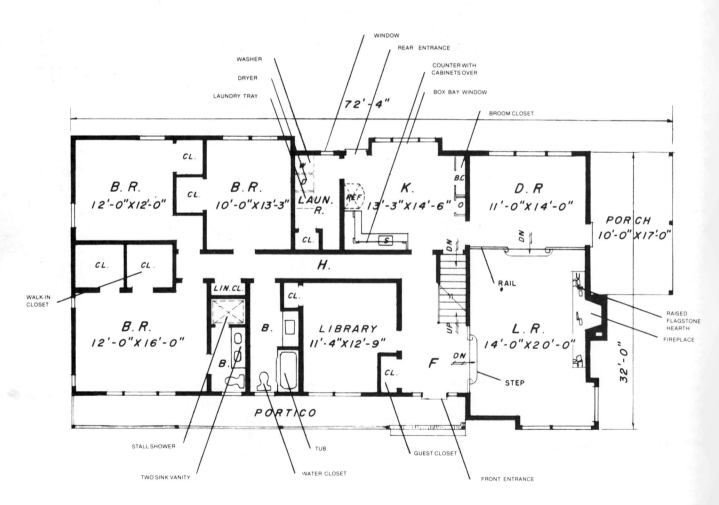

Index

TWO-STORY AND EXPANSION RANCH

Cost, on the basis of amount per square foot, is usually lower for a two-story than for other types of houses. The upstairs bedrooms have more privacy. The two-story should have at least one bath on each floor. More rooms can be built on less land than with any other type.

The expansion ranch is sometimes called a 1½-story house. The half-a-story usually refers to an attic which can be finished at the time of the original construction or later on. This plan often features a master bedroom on the first floor, with children's bedrooms upstairs. Most 1½-story houses have traditional details in the Cape Cod style.

The Glen-Ridge

The exterior of this graceful three-bedroom design presents a blend of picturesque shutters, shingles, and white clapboards. Inside, we discover large, well-designed rooms, each with more than ample window area.

AREA: First floor: 750 sq. ft.
       Second floor: 750 sq. ft.

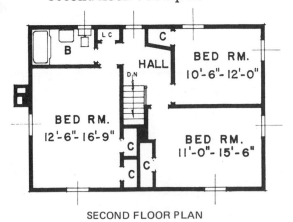

SECOND FLOOR PLAN

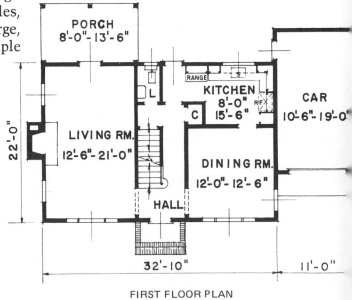

FIRST FLOOR PLAN

The Pinecrest

The two-story plan traditionally signifies "home" to a great many families, especially those whose ideas of comfort require the serenely private atmosphere of the upstairs bedroom.

The stately appearance of this house with its side-lighted entrance, large picture windows, and stone front presents a perfect blend of the traditional and contemporary. The first floor opens through wide archways to the dining room on the left, and on the right to an extra-long living room with fireplace. There is ready access to a large, airy porch on the side.

A door near the rear of the living room leads to a small hall which provides entrance to the lavatory, kitchen, and basement. The kitchen is large enough for a family-size table and provides a pleasant background for informal dining. It is efficiently arranged, with a service door leading to the garage.

Upstairs are three large bedrooms, a bath off the hall, and a separate dressing room in the master bedroom, which provides tremendous clothes space.

AREA: First floor: 754 sq. ft.
Second floor: 754 sq. ft.

SECOND FLOOR PLAN

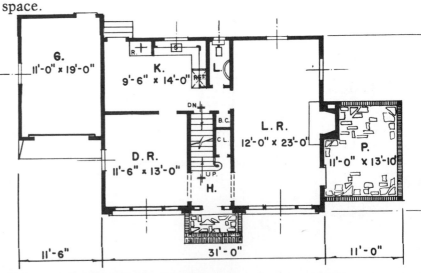

FIRST FLOOR PLAN

The Glen-Dale

Typically colonial, this house offers comfortable living to many families whose needs are as modern as tomorrow. Conveniently grouped around the central stair, this house features a large living room windowed at each end, efficient kitchen large enough for informal family dining, and dining room for formal occasions. The second floor contains four bedrooms and bath with more than ample closets. Enhanced by an attached garage and entrance porch, this house is an asset to any community.

AREA: First floor: 810 sq. ft.
Second floor: 750 sq. ft.

SECOND FLOOR PLAN

BEDROOM 9'-0" X 10'-0"

BEDROOM 10'-1" X 10'-2"

HALL

BEDROOM 12'-0" X 13'-10"

BEDROOM 11'-4" X 13'-5"

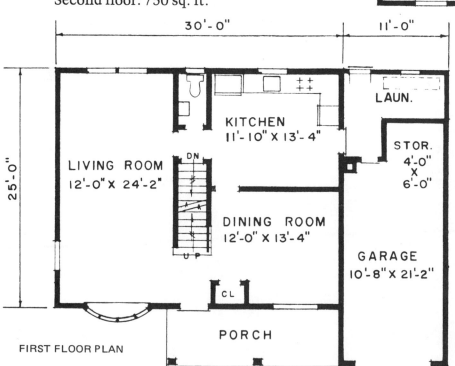

30'-0"

11'-0"

25'-0"

LIVING ROOM 12'-0" X 24'-2"

KITCHEN 11'-10" X 13'-4"

LAUN.

STOR. 4'-0" X 6'-0"

DINING ROOM 12'-0" X 13'-4"

GARAGE 10'-8" X 21'-2"

CL

PORCH

FIRST FLOOR PLAN

The Glen-Field

Touches of the traditional and the new are refreshingly combined in this home to bring the utmost in pleasant living.

There's a handsome picture window in the living room. A door off the fireplace opens out to the spacious, covered, stone porch, and an archway reveals the dining room beyond. Modern convenience is the keynote of the kitchen, and the breakfast area is large and sunny. A downstairs lavatory opens off the back entry. Upstairs, you'll find three large bedrooms, one with a charming dormer over the garage, and a convenient central bathroom. Note the ample closets and the storage room under the eaves at the back.

AREA: First floor: 762 sq. ft.
Second floor: 802 sq. ft.

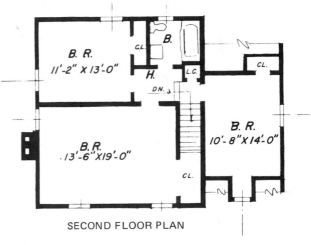

SECOND FLOOR PLAN

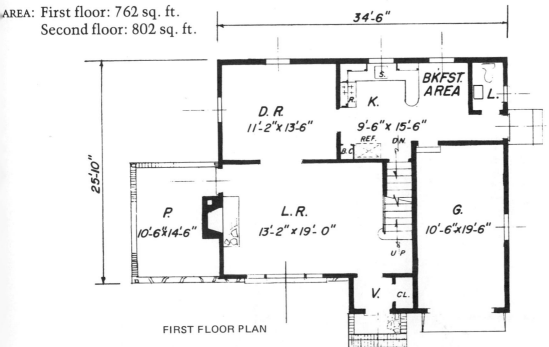

FIRST FLOOR PLAN

The Town-House

This traditional, salt box design is highlighted by a wealth of features including a built-in china closet, snack bar, lavatory, and laundry room adjacent to the kitchen.

Upstairs, three comfortable bedrooms, convenient bath, and lots of closet space provide for the needs of the growing family. A study or additional bedroom and bath can be added at a later date.

AREA: First floor: 704 sq. ft.
Second floor: 704 sq. ft.
Future study & bath: 186 sq. ft.

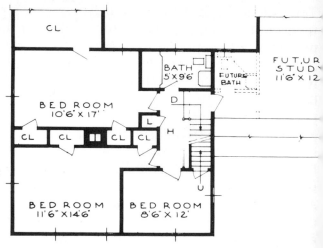

SECOND FLOOR PLAN

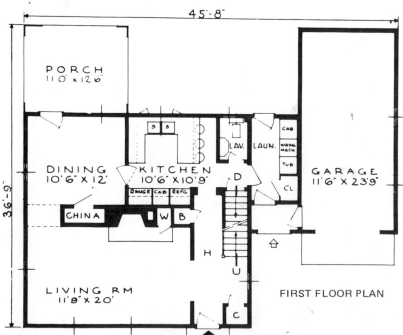

FIRST FLOOR PLAN

The Cedar-Hill

Traditional comfort and contentment are yours with this charming house with the big look.

Notice how successfully the garage blends with the house—Dad will welcome that indoor entrance in wet weather, too. The entry vestibule shields the living room, and the graceful stairway frames a pleasant "decorator" corner for a focal point opposite the fireplace wall. The dining room is charming, and informal meals are perfect in the sunny dining alcove off the kitchen. The cleverly-placed service lavatory doubles as a guest powder room. And the bedrooms provide comfort and privacy on the second floor—see how easily, without any sacrifice or inconvenience, you can have four good-sized bedrooms instead of three, with no loss of storage space.

AREA: First floor: 790 sq. ft.
Second floor: 839 sq. ft.

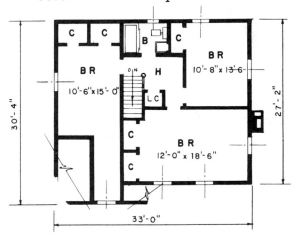

SECOND FLOOR PLAN

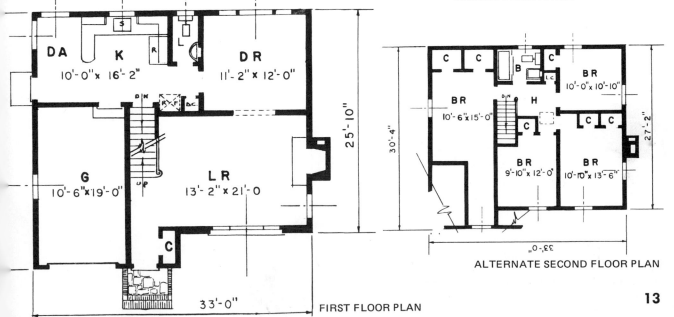

FIRST FLOOR PLAN

ALTERNATE SECOND FLOOR PLAN

13

The Oak-Hill

Here is an economical plan developed in the homey New England salt box style. For those who love the endearing charm of days gone by, we have combined all the conveniences of modern living with the appearance of tradition. Where two bedrooms are sufficient for the immediate needs of a family, this house may be built with the second floor unfinished. Later, when the need arises, the two enormous, second floor rooms may be finished off for children's bedrooms or a play room.

AREA: First floor: 910 sq. ft.
Second floor: 725 sq. ft.

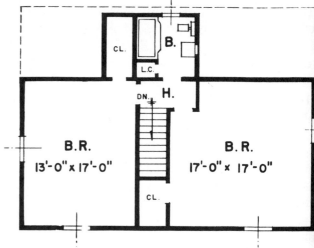

SECOND FLOOR PLAN

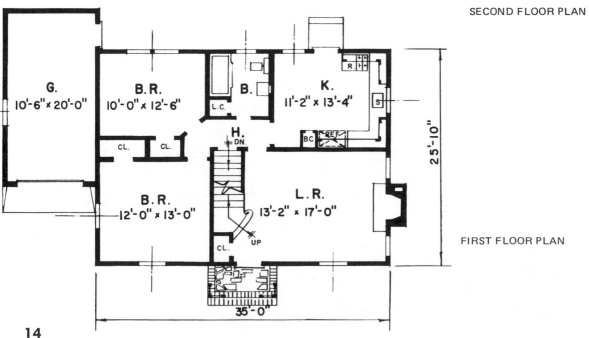

FIRST FLOOR PLAN

The May-Fair

All the charm and comfort of the two-story home are brought out in this economically arranged plan. This home, including an attached garage with separate storage closet, plus a first floor lavatory convenient to rear and garage entrances, can in many areas be constructed on a lot as narrow as 50' by moving the porch to the rear.

Step-saving efficiency is evident in this design, with its entrance hall leading directly to the kitchen and basement-garage door directly opposite the kitchen service door. The second floor provides three wonderful bedrooms with oversize closets, a separate linen closet in the spacious hall, and an exceptionally roomy bath. All bedrooms have cross-ventilation and plenty of wall space for furniture arrangement.

AREA: First floor: 850 sq. ft.
      Second floor: 805 sq. ft.

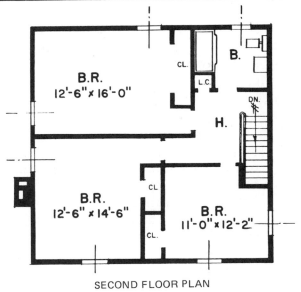

SECOND FLOOR PLAN

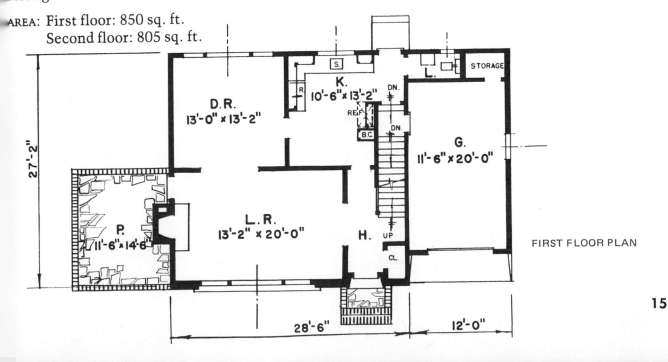

FIRST FLOOR PLAN

The New Haven

A prominent feature of this attractive house is the double bow-windowed facade for living room and dining room. The living room has a large fireplace, too, and a through-view to the back garden. The center hall makes this plan so popular, with all downstairs rooms opening from it. Beside the huge kitchen is a lavatory easily accessible from front and back doors. Upstairs, the three bedrooms are family-sized and the closets more than ample. The master bedroom has its own shower bathroom and two closets, one a walk-in with a window, and a stairway up to storage under the roof. The airy bedrooms each have two exposures, and of course, are large enough for two beds. Charm and practicality combine here for a perfect family home.

AREA: First floor: 840 sq. ft.
Second floor: 840 sq. ft.

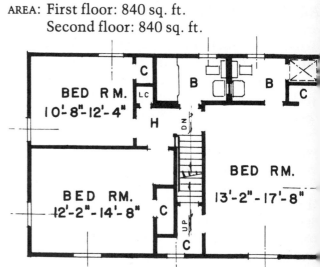

SECOND FLOOR PLAN

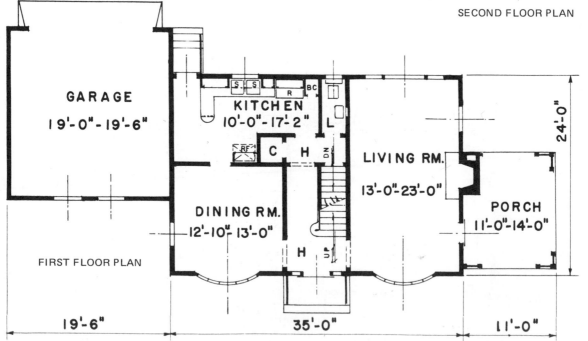

FIRST FLOOR PLAN

The Green-Briar

Brick veneer, beveled siding, shutters, bow window, arch-sheltered entry, and an overhanging second floor all add up to a charming exterior in this four- bedroom, full-basement, two-story house with a modified horizontal appearance.

A dramatic double-door entrance leads through a graceful, open-stair reception area into the warm, wood-paneled family room. The open feeling of the spacious living room and dining room makes entertaining a joy.

The second floor is highlighted by the master bedroom, with its own bath and windowed walk-in closet. Three other bedrooms are well served by a centrally located bath.

AREA: First floor: 925 sq. ft.
    Second floor: 864 sq. ft.

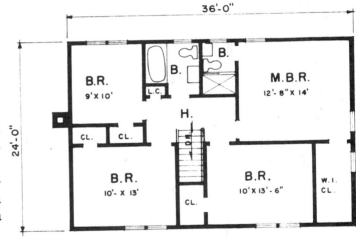

SECOND FLOOR PLAN

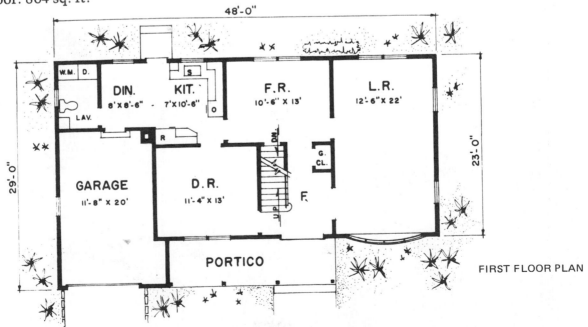

FIRST FLOOR PLAN

The Lynn-Brooke

Here is a charming colonial for the budget-minded. Its center foyer with adjoining lavatory leads directly to all major living areas. Adjacent to the family-size kitchen is a large family room with front and rear exposures, including glass sliding doors opening to the private patio. Just a few steps from the kitchen is a combination laundry-mud room opening directly to the rear yard.

The four bedrooms and two baths on the second floor with generous closets offer ample space for a growing family.

Note the ideal, out-of-the-way storage in the front of the two-car garage.

AREA: First floor: 995 sq. ft.
Second floor: 837 sq. ft.

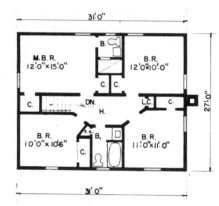

SECOND FLOOR PLAN

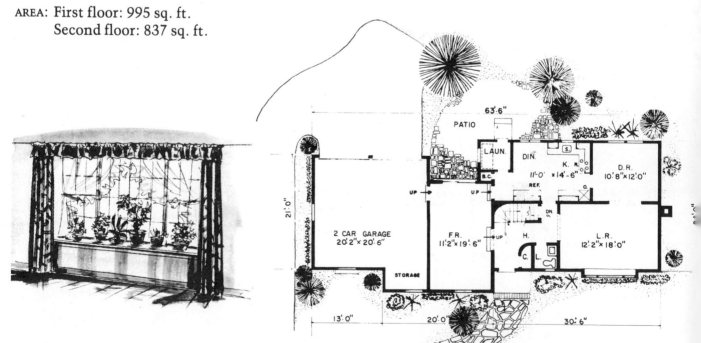

FIRST FLOOR PLAN

18

The Sher-Brooke

This seven-room colonial with attached two-car garage has everything that a family needs. The full-length living room with its distinguished fireplace enjoys three exposures. Note the truly "family-size" kitchen-dinette. Adjacent to the kitchen are the dining room and family room, which has sliding doors leading out to a covered porch and a convenient door to the garage. The first floor lavatory is readily accessible from the outside.

Upstairs are three large bedrooms and two baths, plus seven large closets, highlighted by the large walk-in closet in the master bedroom. This New England colonial with its narrow clapboard and wood shingle exterior would be an asset to any community.

AREA: First floor: 1,030 sq. ft.
Second floor: 805 sq. ft.

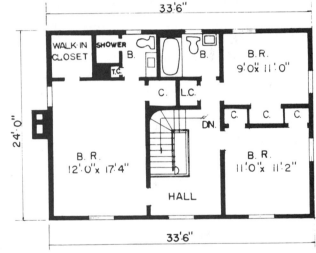

SECOND FLOOR PLAN

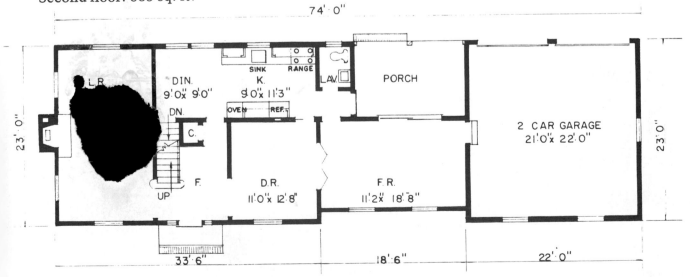

FIRST FLOOR PLAN

The Coolidge

Comfort and elegance, the traditional hallmarks of the two-story home, are readily apparent in this home.

The fieldstone and siding exterior features a picturesque planter which complements the breezeway.

The attractive first floor comprises a bow-windowed living room with fireplace, dining room, and step-saving kitchen with adjoining lavatory.

Three large, cross-ventilated bedrooms with ample closets and two full baths make up the second floor.

AREA: First floor: 924 sq. ft.
Second floor: 957 sq. ft.

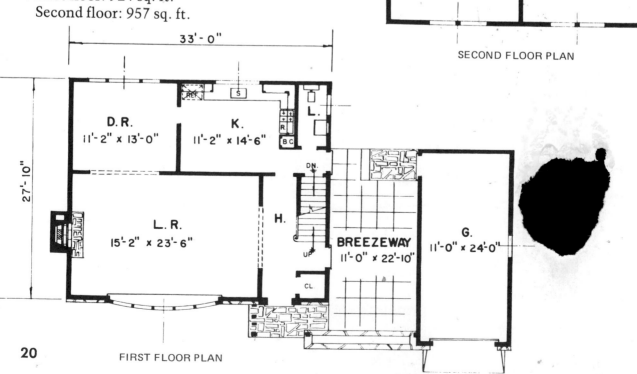

SECOND FLOOR PLAN

FIRST FLOOR PLAN

The Dell-Wood

This well-planned four-bedroom home will delight the family who needs plenty of living space, but has only a small lot.

The good design of the kitchen-dinette and adjoining dining room makes serving an ease. The spacious living room with a fireplace calls for relaxation.

There are four large bedrooms on the second floor with ample closets for all. The extra-large closet in front could be converted to a private bath for the master bedroom.

Practicality highlights this efficient design, which will fit on most small lots.

AREA: First floor: 899 sq. ft. (excluding garage)
Second floor: 990 sq. ft.

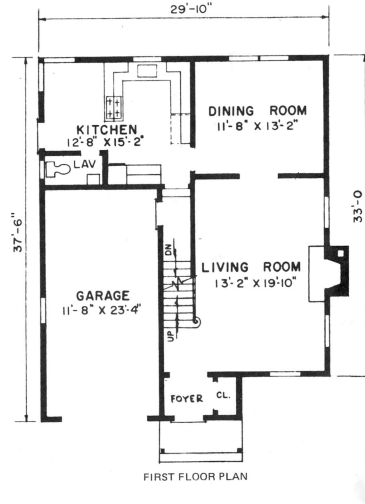

FIRST FLOOR PLAN

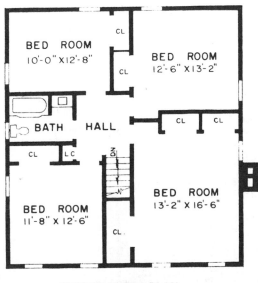

SECOND FLOOR PLAN

The New-Vernon

Modern efficiency is featured in this fine two-story home within a perfect, traditional plan. Classic in its simplicity, the living room has a bonus of picture windows front and back, a magnificent fireplace, and access to the den. The warm, inviting den can be put at the rear, if your lot is narrow. Across the hall, there's the hospitality-minded dining room, and at the back, the kitchen is pleasantly spacious, with a lavatory only a few steps away.

Upstairs, big, airy bedrooms, three of them, are well-supplied with closets. A private shower bathroom for the master suite is supplemented by a second bathroom.

AREA: First floor: 1,029 sq. ft.
Second floor: 870 sq. ft.

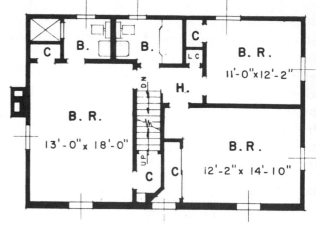

SECOND FLOOR PLAN

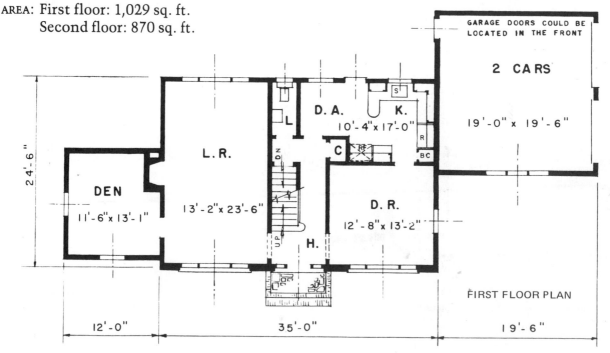

FIRST FLOOR PLAN

The Glenbrook

Convenience is added to the valued privacy afforded in this two-story plan by incorporating a built-in two-car garage and lavatory directly adjacent to the service entrance. A modern touch is given to the interior by opening the dining room to the living room, thereby creating the effect of spaciousness from front to rear with an unbroken area 29 ' long. The addition of a room over the garage provides ample space for a child's playroom or an extra room for guests—a total of four bedrooms in all.

AREA: First floor: 885 sq. ft.
Second floor: 1,050 sq. ft.

SECOND FLOOR PLAN

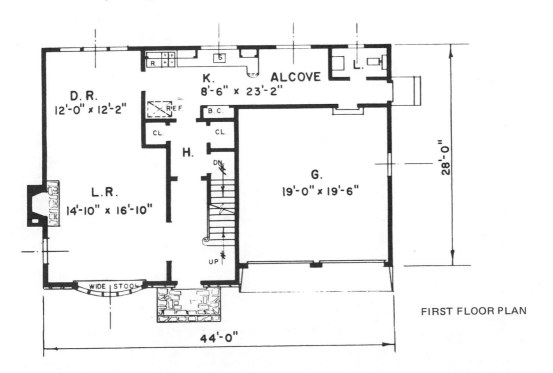

FIRST FLOOR PLAN

The Westminster

The Tudor adaptation of this three-bedroom, two-story design will make it stand out as a home of distinction. Its elegant exterior appearance is matched only by the quality of the interior design, which was created for the modern family.

Inside, the unusually large foyer, with its two coat closets, makes a fine reception area and is the key to efficient circulation, distributing traffic effectively throughout the first floor and by an attractive staircase to the two bedrooms on the second floor. To the left is the formal dining room.

The oak-paneled family room directly behind the living room features a stone fireplace with a raised, flagstone hearth flanked by casement windows on either side.

There is no doubt that the romance and rustic charm of the English half-timber style of this three-bedroom, two-story design should delight families with a taste for continental design.

AREA: First floor: 1,458 sq. ft.
Second floor: 539 sq. ft.
Basement: 1,458 sq. ft.
Garage & Laundry: 639 sq. ft.

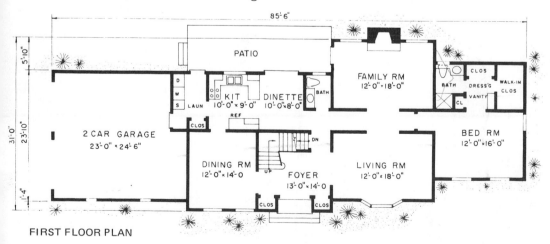

FIRST FLOOR PLAN

SECOND FLOOR PLAN

The Coventry

This charming Tudor adaptation, reminiscent of Old England, could hardly be improved. Its fine proportions and exquisite use of exterior materials of half-timber, stucco, multi-paned windows, and steep-hipped, trimmed circular entrance result in a most distinctive home. Even the attached garage with its hipped dormer, diamond-shaped window, and extended wall adds impact to this design.

Designed to contribute to a feeling of personal luxury, the master bedroom suite has a dressing area with three closets and a private bath with mirrored vanity and tiled shower stall.

Each of the other three bedrooms is served by the main bath, which has a tub and a full-length mirrored vanity.

AREA: First floor: 1,082 sq. ft.
Second floor: 916 sq. ft.
Garage: 506 sq. ft.
Patio: 160 sq. ft.

SECOND FLOOR PLAN

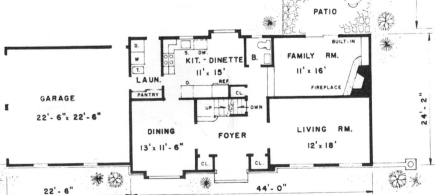

FIRST FLOOR PLAN

The Eton

The rediscovered charm of this Tudor design is reminiscent of the quiet dignity and flavor of early English country living. This bygone style has returned to popularity and the architectural features are many: added timbers on stucco walls, massive brick chimney with protruding chimney pots, wavy siding, steep roofs of varying heights, and diamond-paned windows.

Although this home looks quite impressive from the outside, it is not quite as expensive to build as it looks.

The octagonal central tower which accommodates the entrance foyer is larger than some rooms; this two-story, full basement, three-bedroom house will comfortably meet the needs of the average family for present-day living.

AREA: First floor: 1,182 sq. ft.
Second floor: 818 sq. ft.
Basement: 962 sq. ft.
Garage: 662 sq. ft.

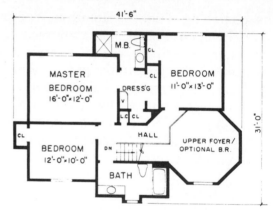

SECOND FLOOR PLAN

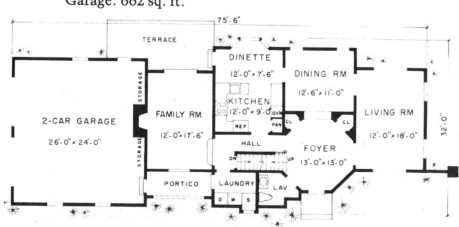

FIRST FLOOR PLAN

The Ferndale

The three-level entry of this staggered roofline two-story house produces unusually good traffic patterns. Distinction is added by the warm combination of hand-split shingles, clerestory windows, and random-width fieldstone veneer. The entrance foyer acts as a central distribution point; from there you can go down two steps to the living room, down three steps to the family room and dining-kitchen area, or walk upstairs to the four bedrooms on the second floor.

The comfort and convenience of this design are as modern as tomorrow.

AREA: First floor: 1,196 sq. ft.
Second floor: 808 sq. ft.

SECOND FLOOR PLAN

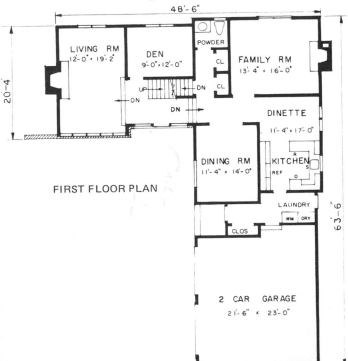

FIRST FLOOR PLAN

The Oak-Ridge

Typically New England colonial, this two-story home has all the conventional characteristics of yesterday's appearance plus all the modern conveniences of today's planning and equipment.

The built-in garage and den wing also contains a convenient powder room for guests plus space above for an additional bedroom, which could be left unfinished to provide for a growing family.

The main body of the house contains a modern working kitchen with dinette space, a full-sized dining room and living room, all serviced by a through-hall entry. Upstairs are three good-sized bedrooms and two baths; plenty of closets and the future fourth bedroom complete this well-designed plan.

AREA: First floor: 950 sq. ft. (excluding porch and garage)
Second floor: 1,058 sq. ft.

SECOND FLOOR PLAN

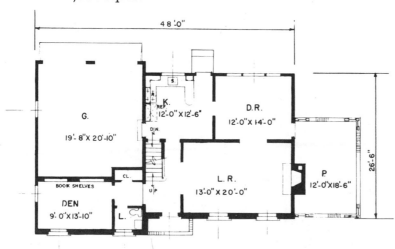

FIRST FLOOR PLAN

The New-Windsor

This half-timber, English Tudor-inspired two-story design looks large and luxurious from the outside, and that same feeling of size is carried throughout the plan.

Just off the spacious entrance foyer is the all-purpose family room with a "wet bar" conveniently located off the kitchen-dinette for guest entertaining.

An open-well staircase leads to the upstairs four bedrooms and two baths. Of special interest on the second floor is the spare room area over the garage, which may be used as a fifth bedroom, hobby, or recreation room.

AREA: First floor: 1,390 sq. ft.
Second floor: 1,828 sq. ft.
Garage: 655 sq. ft.
Laundry: 63 sq. ft.

SECOND FLOOR PLAN

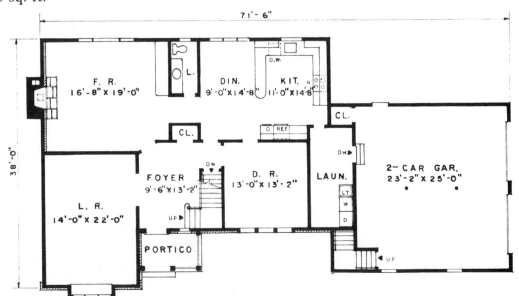

FIRST FLOOR PLAN

The Strathmore

The fine proportions of this impressive exterior, with its stone and brick veneer, half-timber, stucco, half-dormers, diamond and multi-paned windows, are distinctively English and identify the Tudor heritage of this two-story, four-bedroom design. Adding impact are the stone-trimmed, arched entrance, massive brick chimney, and the extended decorative wall.

Visual variety, so pleasing outside, is continued indoors with a breathtaking array of highlights that will cater to the whims of a large family.

Designed to contribute to a feeling of personal luxury, the lavish, secluded master bedroom suite has a dressing area with three closets and a private bath with mirrored vanity and a glass-enclosed, tiled shower stall.

Each of the other three bedrooms is of modest size and is served by the main bath.

AREA: First floor: 1,094 sq. ft.
Second floor: 934 sq. ft.
Garage: 506 sq. ft.
Patio: 160 sq. ft.

SECOND FLOOR PLAN

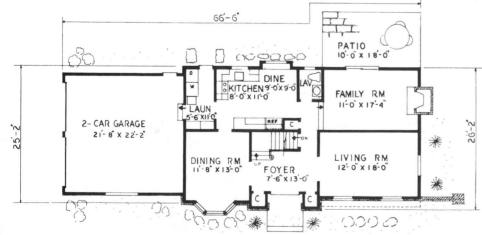

FIRST FLOOR PLAN

The Cedar-Wood

This stately, narrow-clapboard and vertical batten traditional home is a comfortable one, built around a family which enjoys the traditional pleasures: a warm fireplace in the family room, a holiday meal in the formal dining room, or a friendly party in the large living room.

This four-bedroom design reflects the comfort built within, and its exterior makes it right at home in the city, suburb, or country. The wood-paneled family room, with its brick fireplace, has access to the paved patio; the bay-windowed breakfast room provides a cheerful addition to the kitchen.

Inside, the unusually large and impressive foyer is the key to efficient circulation, distributing traffic effectively throughout the first floor and the second floor bedrooms.

For all-around privacy and economy of two-story construction, this plan is ideal for a growing family with a taste for traditional flavor.

AREA: First floor: 1,102 sq. ft.
Second floor: 931 sq. ft.

SECOND FLOOR PLAN

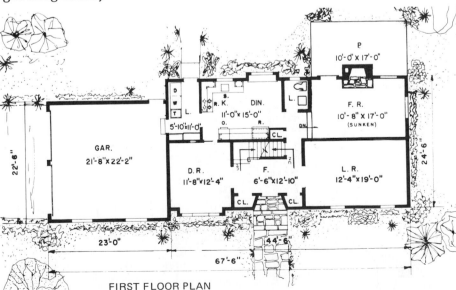

FIRST FLOOR PLAN

The Wakefield

The authentic detailing of the brick arches, leaded glass doors and windows, brick quoins, hip roof, and massive chimney reflects the taste and traditional character of the ever-popular French Provincial style. The exterior of this two-story, three-bedroom design is reminiscent of the country estates of the by-gone era, while the interior combines the formal with the casual for a truly comfortable home for the entire family.

Inside the recessed double doors, the large foyer makes a fine reception area with an impressive staircase and wrought-iron handrail leading to the two bedrooms on the second floor.

Although the exterior of this inviting house recalls another era, the interior offers modern day comfort and convenient living.

AREA: First floor: 1,514 sq. ft.
Second floor: 536 sq. ft.
Basement: 1,580 sq. ft.
Garage & laundry: 618 sq. ft.
Patio: 250 sq. ft.

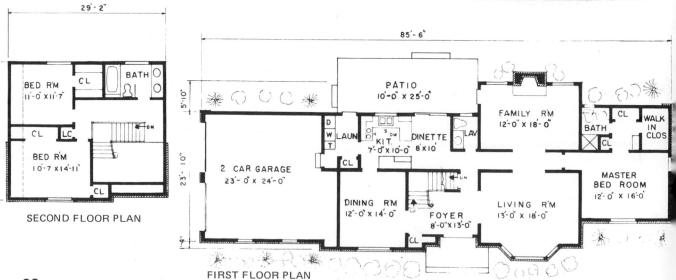

SECOND FLOOR PLAN

FIRST FLOOR PLAN

The Lowell

One of the most interesting characteristics of the popular Dutch colonial is the "Queen Anne," which features the space-creating gambrel room of two different angles and the dormer windows in the lower of the two roof slopes.

Inside, the elevated living room, three steps above the main living level, creates a dramatic balcony view of the dining room with its decorative wrought-iron railing, cathedral ceiling, and lovely box-bayed window.

The three roof dormers enrich the old-fashioned enchantment of this four-bedroom Dutch colonial design.

AREA: First floor: 1,176 sq. ft.
　　　Second floor: 896 sq. ft.

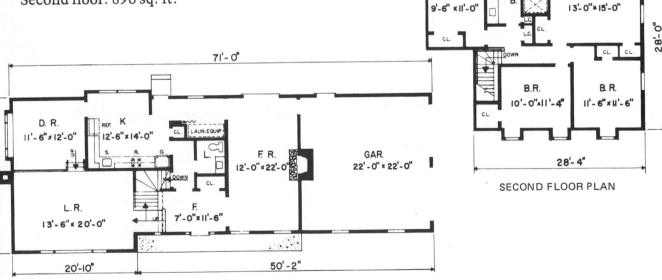

SECOND FLOOR PLAN

FIRST FLOOR PLAN

The North-Gate

Here is a charming garrison colonial for the budget-minded. Its center foyer with adjoining lavatory leads directly to all major living areas. The spacious kitchen with bay-window overlooking the rear garden is a focal point for family living. Adjoining the kitchen is a family room with glass sliding doors opening to the rear patio. Just steps away is a combination laundry-mud room containing three individual closets.

The four bedrooms and two baths on the second floor with generous closets offer ample space for a growing family.

AREA: First floor: 1,112 sq. ft.
Second floor: 960 sq. ft.

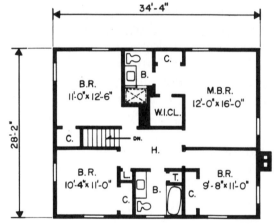

SECOND FLOOR PLAN

34'-4"

28'-2"

B.R. 11'-0" x 12'-6"

M.B.R. 12'-0" x 16'-0"

C.

B.

W.I.CL.

C.

DN.

H.

B.R. 10'-4" x 11'-0"

B.R. 9'-8" x 11'-0"

C.

B.

T.

C.

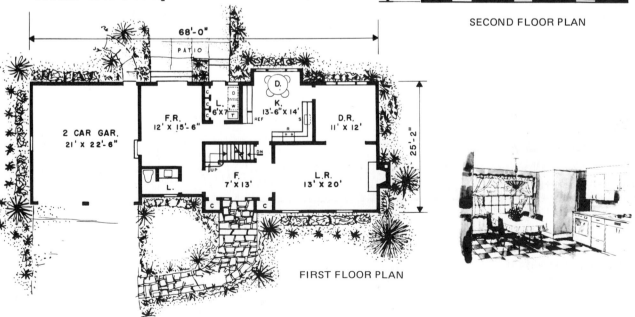

FIRST FLOOR PLAN

68'-0"

25'-2"

PATIO

2 CAR GAR. 21' X 22'-6"

F.R. 12' X 15'-6"

K. 13'-6" X 14'

D.R. 11' X 12'

F. 7' X 13'

L.R. 13' X 20'

L.

The Wynnewood

Adherents of the two-story design will find much to admire in this four-bedroom house of casual contemporary styling which will set it apart from all others in the neighborhood in a strikingly lovely way. The brick planter in front of the plate glass picture window of the living room, the vertical boarding exterior, the sunroof over the entry court, and the interior layout give it a totally "today" look, but its beauty is classic.

Guests enter through a partially covered area between the attached, two-car garage and the house, into a spacious foyer which leads to a sunken living room to add even more grandeur.

Upstairs, the four bedrooms complete a plan which retains all the good qualities of modern living. The master suite has cross-ventilation, a basined and mirrored vanity, three closets, one a walk-in, and a complete tiled bath with vanity and a glass-enclosed stall shower.

The Spartan simplicity of this contemporary, low-pitched room two-story design can provide the ultimate in modern living, at home in any surrounding, in any part of the country.

AREA: First floor: 1,044 sq. ft.
Second floor: 1,040 sq. ft.
Basement: 1,044 sq. ft.
Garage: 528 sq. ft.

2078270

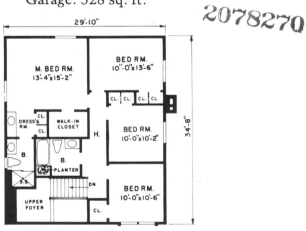

SECOND FLOOR PLAN

FIRST FLOOR PLAN

The Knoll-Wood

Colonial elegance at its finest is provided by this two-story design.

Gabled dormers, picturesque shutters, and a box bay-window arrangement are but a few of the features that this traditional home offers.

The open areas of the first floor make entertaining a joy. Traffic is distributed effectively from the moment one steps inside the door.

Upstair, four bedrooms, each with more than ample closet space, and two bathrooms offer comfort and privacy to the family.

AREA: First floor: 1,135 sq. ft.
Second floor: 990 sq. ft.

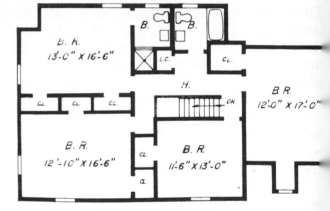

SECOND FLOOR PLAN

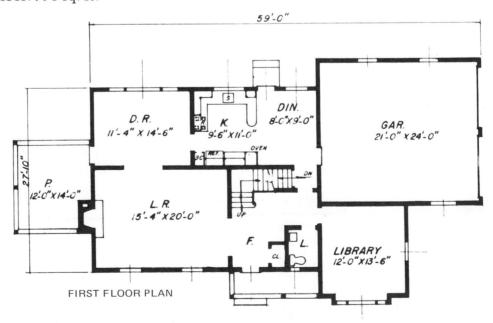

FIRST FLOOR PLAN

The East-Lynne

This home is complete and designed to satisfy all family demands while fitting a low building budget. Its four bedrooms make it a home which would be hard to outgrow. Room arrangement is the essence of efficiency, and the rooms are of a size and shape needed to handle their assignments.

Added formality is given to the living and dining rooms by the large and impressive main foyer, which circulates traffic throughout the first floor areas and second floor bedrooms.

The combined family room, kitchen, and dinette offer more than 15' of width across the back. A few steps away are the laundry room and a convenient lavatory near the family room.

All the bedrooms have cross-ventilation and are liberally supplied with closets. The master bedroom has a private full bath with stall shower and an angular, full-wall mirrored vanity.

AREA: First floor: 1,167 sq. ft.
Second floor: 959 sq. ft.

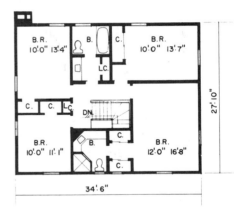

SECOND FLOOR PLAN

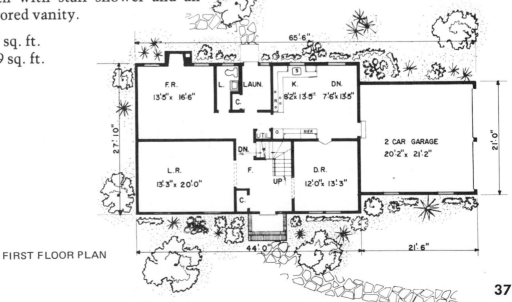

FIRST FLOOR PLAN

The Brook-Dale

The distinctive character of the Old Southern colonial mansion is expressed in the exterior of this proud two-story home. This shell of tradition holds a modern architectural gem of planning for modern living.

At the entrance, we find an ingenious recessed design to afford weather protection for the front door. The eye-catching open stair and wrought-iron rail form a delightful background for the foyer. Just steps away are the powder room and private den. To the rear is a kitchen designed in the most modern, step-saving style, complete with breakfast area. A dining room, tremendous living room, and airy porch complete the first floor.

Upstairs are four bedrooms sized in keeping with the stately air of this home. Closets are in abundance, and two full baths complete this second floor area. Note that the garage is built-in under the house. This feature is economical, as well as practical for lot size or contour as required.

AREA: First floor: 1,140 sq. ft.
   Second floor: 1,085 sq. ft.

SECOND FLOOR PLAN

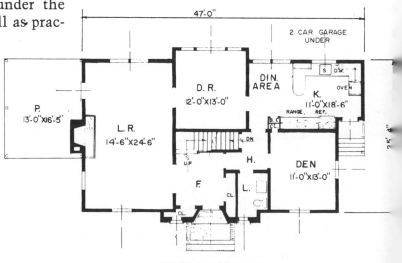

FIRST FLOOR PLAN

The River-Crest

Nobody has yet come up with a more economical way of housing a large family on a modest lot than with a two-story residence, and in these days of rising land prices, the financial advantage of one set of rooms atop another is greater than ever.

Inside, the central foyer distributes traffic effectively throughout the first floor. On the second floor, the family's needs are well served by four bedrooms, two baths, and lots of closets.

Typical of many houses built during the colonial days, this four-bedroom house has the traditional small-paned, shuttered windows, and beveled red cedar clapboards accented with vertical corner boards for a general air of comfort and hospitality.

AREA: First floor: 1,145 sq. ft.
      Second floor: 1,145 sq. ft.

SECOND FLOOR PLAN

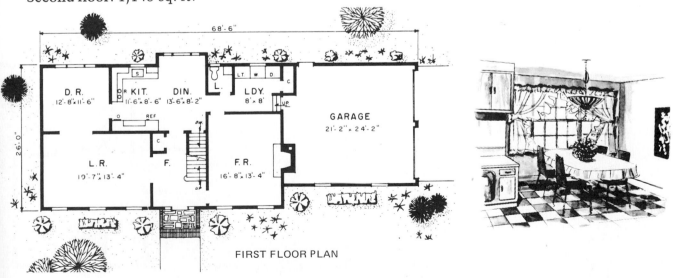

FIRST FLOOR PLAN

The Belle-Terre

This masterpiece of luxury and comfort has been created for those who want the best in traditional two-story living.

The front door of this stately home opens into a cozy foyer with a convenient guest closet and a lavatory, which may also serve as a powder room. A picturesque arch leads form the foyer to the bright and cheery living room, which boasts a friendly hearth and large windows at each end. The dining room, highlighted by a beautiful picture window, is conveniently located next to a large, modern kitchen which includes a dining area. Completing the first floor is an inviting den designed for reading or for just plain relaxing.

Upstairs, remote from the activity of the floor below, we find four big bedrooms and two full baths. Many closets and a two-car garage complete this design for gracious living.

AREA: First floor: 1,140 sq. ft.
Second floor: 1,100 sq. ft.

SECOND FLOOR PLAN

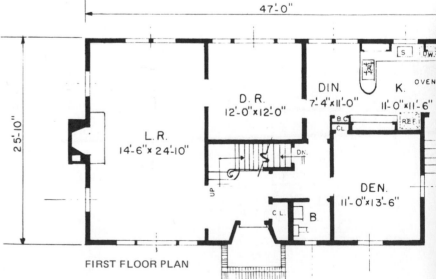

FIRST FLOOR PLAN

The New-Englander

The contemporary interpretation of this plan recalls the stately homes of New England with the emphasis on solid comfort and balanced proportions.

The first floor lends itself to easy, relaxed family living; the spacious family room and living room cater to the needs of the active family.

On the second floor, there are four comfortable bedrooms, highlighted by a master bedroom with walk-in closet, built-in vanity, and private bathroom with stall shower.

AREA: First floor: 1,162 sq. ft.
Second floor: 1,118 sq. ft.

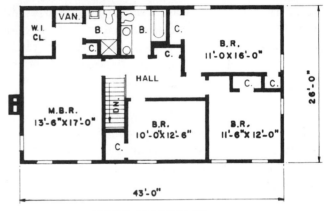

SECOND FLOOR PLAN

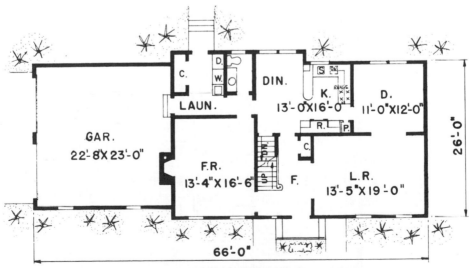

FIRST FLOOR PLAN

The Park-Lane

Here is an expandable two-story colonial design. The future fourth bedroom directly off the second floor foyer can also be used as a den or children's playroom. This room can be finished with only minor expense as the need arises.

Within a few steps of all bedrooms is the main family "split" bath with toilet and tub separated from the vanitory area. This vanity area, with wall-to-wall mirror, built-in planter, and towel cabinet, is unsurpassed for convenience.

The living areas, with interconnecting traffic flow plus a conveniently located powder room and laundry, allow for excellent formal or informal entertaining.

A spacious basement with incorporated two-car garage allows this home to be built on most of today's minimum-sized building sites.

AREA: First floor: 1,390 sq. ft.
Second floor: 918 sq. ft.

SECOND FLOOR PLAN

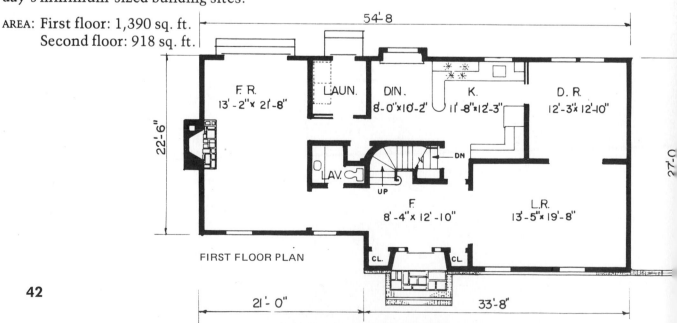

FIRST FLOOR PLAN

The Madison

True stone veneer and white shingles, plus an enchanting plant bed and the extended garage roof line, give this house its distinctive appeal.

The interior carries out this appeal with emphasis. Note the separate vestibule with a guest closet, the main hall, which has access to all rooms on the first floor, and the beautiful, open staircase to the bedrooms on the second floor.

There is a wonderfully large living room with an over-size fireplace, picture windows front and rear and, through doors on either side of the fireplace, a study and porch. There is a lavatory easily accessible from kitchen and living room. The spacious kitchen has loads of counter space, a separate dining alcove, a serving bar, and a service entrance.

The second floor is a dream, with lots of floor space and closets—four bedrooms and nine big closets, plus a full-size staircase to the attic for extra storage space.

AREA: First floor: 1,228 sq. ft.
Second floor: 1,087 sq. ft.

SECOND FLOOR PLAN

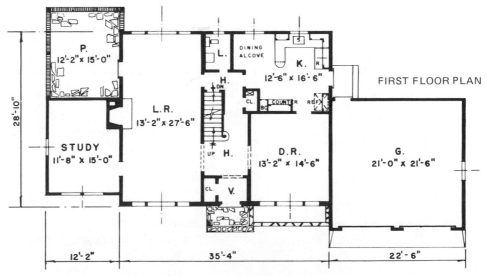

FIRST FLOOR PLAN

The Old-Greenwich

The gambrel roof, front facade of handsplit red cedar shakes, small-paned windows, paneled entrance doors with sidelights, shed-roof dormers, and large chimney add to the free interpretation of this eight-room, two-story design.

The first floor arrangement provides a central entry hall around which all the primary living areas are oriented within an area of 1,145 square feet.

An attractive staircase leads from the entrance foyer to the second floor comfort of four bedrooms and two baths. The master bedroom provides a relaxing atmosphere, with its dressing room, walk-in closet, and private stall-shower bathroom. The other three bedrooms are amply served by a convenient, central bathroom.

This is a good, practical and attractive house with comfort and livability built in.

AREA: First floor: 1,145 sq. ft.
Second floor: 1,145 sq. ft.

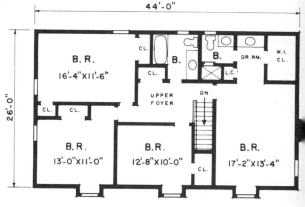

SECOND FLOOR PLAN

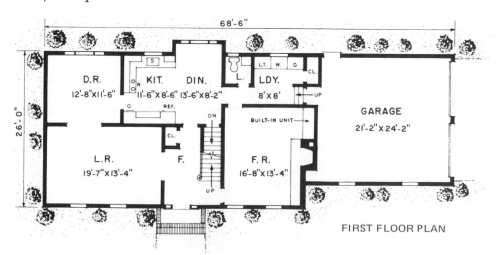

FIRST FLOOR PLAN

The New-Milford

One of the most interesting variations of the colonial design is the New England salt box. It is distinguished from its sister houses mainly because of its rear roof lines, which extend downward much lower than the front roof lines.

Although the living room has four windows, it also has plenty of wall space for imaginative decorating, and it features a brick-faced, log-burning fireplace. The combined kitchen-family room affords enough space for informal meals and relaxation.

Three of the four bedrooms are close to the family bathroom, the master bedroom has two sliding door closets, four windows, and a bath with a glass-enclosed shower stall and full-length mirrored dressing vanity.

This is a good, solid house, without frills but with comfort and livability built in.

AREA: First floor: 1,250 sq. ft.
Second floor: 1,078 sq. ft.

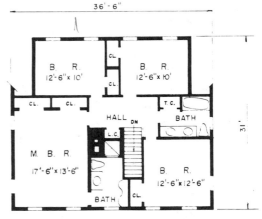

SECOND FLOOR PLAN

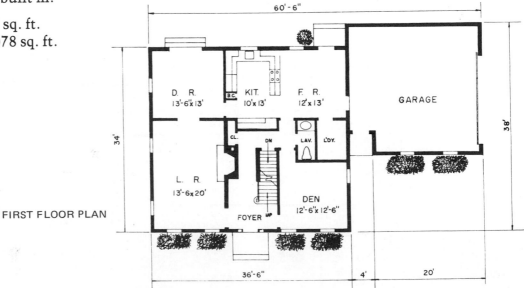

FIRST FLOOR PLAN

The Short-Hills

This is truly a southern colonial with its large portico and square columns.

The curved staircase leading to the second floor foyer, family room with incorporated bar, and first floor den are only a few of the highlights of this plan.

A skillfully-planned kitchen with window-walls surrounding the dinette affords a picturesque view while dining.

The master bedroom has a rear window wall and door which leads to a sitting balcony overlooking the rear garden. Completing the second floor, the remaining three large bedrooms and hall bath will satisfy any family's needs.

AREA: First floor: 1,371 sq. ft.
Second floor: 960 sq. ft.

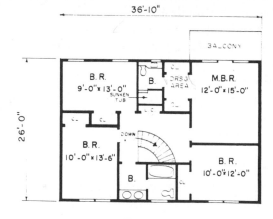

SECOND FLOOR PLAN

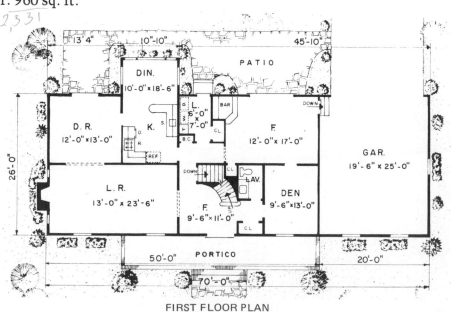

FIRST FLOOR PLAN

The Wood-Gate

This 18th century Dutch colonial exterior cloaks a 20th century floor plan.

Ideal traffic circulation is evident in this colonial design. The large living room, which measures 13' by 24', has three exterior exposures and a colonial fireplace. The laundry, located just a few steps from the kitchen, with its closet, counter work area, and separate entrance, is a must in today's colonial homes. This area will surely satisfy the family's needs.

A second fireplace is located in the family room, which is accessible from the kitchen or dining room. The sliding glass doors tend to bring the outdoors in for that much-desired "indoor-outdoor" living.

On the second floor, note the size (6' by 9') of the master bedroom walk-in closet with built-in shelves and shoe racks. The remaining three bedrooms are all twin size with liberal closet space. They are complemented by the two back-to-back bathrooms.

AREA: First floor: 1,365 sq. ft.
Second floor: 1,030 sq. ft.

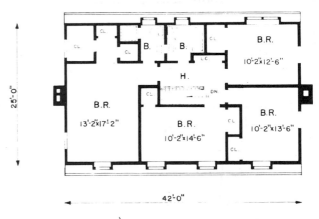

SECOND FLOOR PLAN

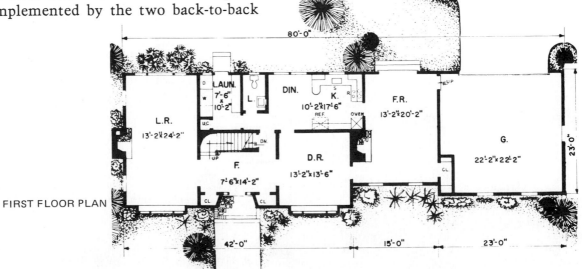

FIRST FLOOR PLAN

The Donny-Brooke

This New England L-shaped colonial design, with its exterior of wood shingles and vertical siding, is surely an "eye-catcher."

From the entrance foyer, there is ideal circulation to all principal first floor areas along an open staircase leading to the four second floor bedrooms.

The master bedroom, with private bath, dressing area, and sit-down vanity, along with its large walk-in closet, becomes a suite of its own.

The women of the house will be overjoyed with the large, family-size kitchen which this plan offers. The dinette in itself is larger than many dining rooms and will easily seat six. Connecting the kitchen and garage, as well as leading directly to the front and rear yards, is a spacious laundry room.

Note the wood-paneled study with its own fireplace and closet. It is an ideal spot for relaxing by one and all.

AREA: First floor: 1,345 sq. ft.
Second floor: 1,064 sq. ft.

SECOND FLOOR PLAN

FIRST FLOOR PLAN

The Wickham-Woods

Few styles of residential architecture have the comfortable warmth of the houses built in America during the early 19th century. The secret lay in their simplicity. This design has many of the early earmarks: the big chimney, hand-split wood shingles, small-paned windows with shutters, and paneled entrance door.

Inside, the plan shifts to the 20th century with step-saving physical comfort and convenient traffic control. The big kitchen-dinette has a full complement of cabinets and appliances, plus a picture window dinette. A spacious foyer, living room, dining room, powder room, family room, and laundry complete the first floor.

Upstairs are four bedrooms with ample closets and two full baths.

AREA: First floor: 1,340 sq. ft.
Second floor: 1,070 sq. ft.
Garage: 590 sq. ft.

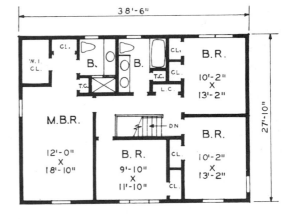

SECOND FLOOR PLAN

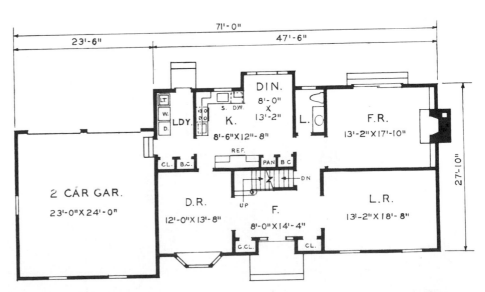

FIRST FLOOR PLAN

The Deer-Field

Ideal traffic circulation is evident in this colonial design. The large living room, which measures 13' by 24', has three exterior exposures and a colonial fireplace. A "must" in today's homes is the laundry, located just a few steps from the kitchen and leading directly to the outdoors; it also has a closet and counter work area.

A second fireplace is located in the family room, which is accessible from the kitchen or dining room. The large sliding glass doors tend to bring the outdoors in for that much desired "indoor-outdoor" living.

On the second floor, note the size (6' by 9') of the master bedroom walk-in closet with built-in shelves and show racks. The remaining three bedrooms are all twin size, with liberal closet space.

AREA: First floor: 1,365 sq. ft.
Second floor: 1,050 sq. ft.

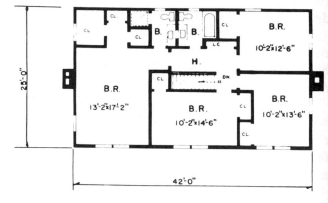

SECOND FLOOR PLAN

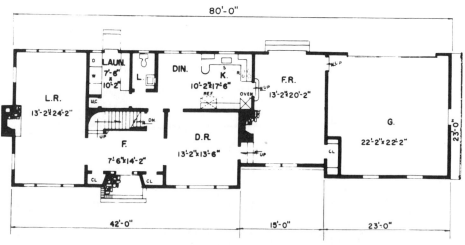

FIRST FLOOR PLAN

The York-Towne

Here is a home with exterior charm of the 18th century which fulfills the requirements of modern residential layouts.

The combined kitchen-breakfast room arrangement offers more than 18 feet of width across the back of the house; a few steps away is the laundry room with its separate entry.

Both the formal living room and dining room are well suited to various furniture arrangements. Off the entrance foyer are a lavatory and open stair. The family room has pine-paneled walls, brick fireplace, and sliding glass doors to the outdoor terrace.

On the second floor, three bedrooms are close to the main family bath. The master bedroom suite has two large walk-in closets, and a private compartmented bath with tiled shower stall and counter vanity.

AREA: First floor: 1,356 sq. ft.
Second floor: 1,060 sq. ft.

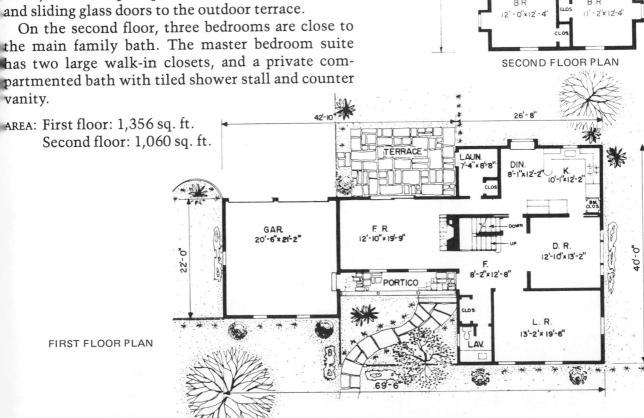

SECOND FLOOR PLAN

FIRST FLOOR PLAN

The Manor

When it is desired to create a good first impression in a house of moderate size, the graceful character of the French Provincial is often the answer.

The basic plan, consisting of four bedrooms and 2½ baths, is rectangular to keep costs down and has a habitable area on the two floors of 2,420 square feet.

Its combination of hand-split red cedar shingles, brick veneer with the brick-quoined corners, diamond-paned windows over the recessed entrance, and the hipped roofs will be stylish for many years to come.

An interesting feature is the unusually large and impressive foyer, which makes a fine reception area, with two coat closets; this foyer is the key to efficient circulation, distributing traffic effectively throughout the first floor living area and, by an open stair rail, to the second floor bedrooms.

AREA: First floor: 1,224 sq. ft.
Second floor: 1,111 sq. ft.
Laundry: 85 sq. ft.
Garage: 517 sq. ft.
Basement: 1,306 sq. ft.

SECOND FLOOR PLAN

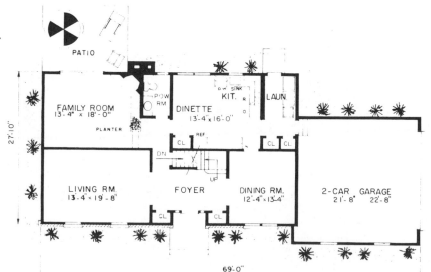

FIRST FLOOR PLAN

The Chevy-Chase

There are no fancy features to this two-story variation of an Early American house, but there is a definite feeling of solidity and warmth that suggests comfortable living and a rectangular design which cuts construction costs. Of special interest is the sizeable entrance foyer, which is more than 14′ wide and makes a fine reception area.

On the second floor, the master bedroom offers comfort and privacy with its walk-in closet and private bathroom. The other three bedrooms are serviced by a centrally located bath.

The house makes maximum use of every square foot of space on the inside and has old-fashioned charm on the outside.

AREA: First floor: 1,375 sq. ft.
       Second floor: 1,060 sq. ft.

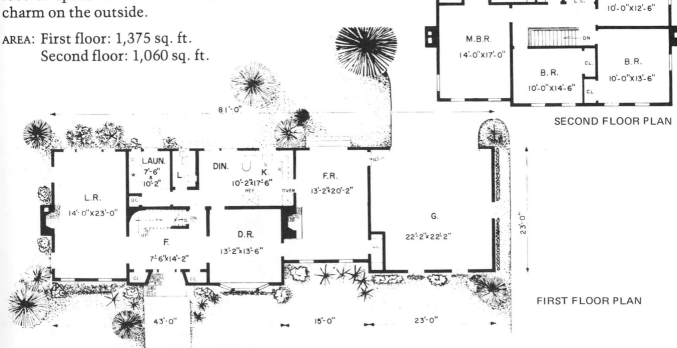

SECOND FLOOR PLAN

FIRST FLOOR PLAN

53

The New-Castle

The imposing exterior of this French Provincial will stand out in any neighborhood. This architectural style, derived from native French architecture, has held its popularity throughout the years. Design elements which contribute to the attractive exterior appearance of the house are the curved brick door and window heads, the continuous dentil moulding around the eave of the roof, and the louvred cupola over the garage.

An attractive staircase leads directly from the entrance foyer to the four bedrooms on the second floor. The master bedroom suite has a full bath and two closets, one of which is a double walk-in. Each of the other three bedrooms is amply supplied with closet space, a total of seven closets on the second floor.

A corner brick fireplace with a raised hearth and sliding glass doors to the rear patio highlight the family room.

AREA: First floor: 1,317 sq. ft.
Second floor: 1,123 sq. ft.

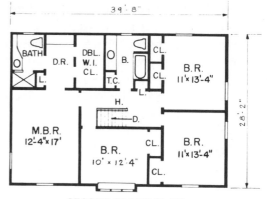

SECOND FLOOR PLAN

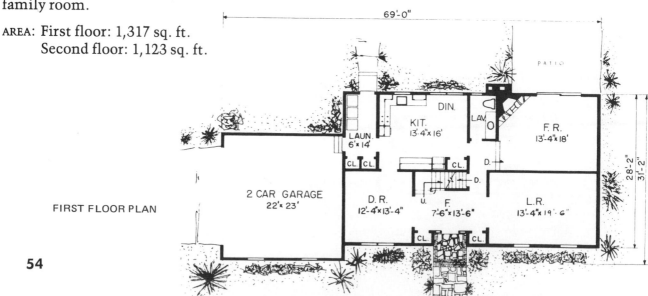

FIRST FLOOR PLAN

54

The Pine-Wood

All the regal luxury of the traditional two-story home is contained in the contemporary styling of this large, eight-room plan.

The front of this home presents long, low-appearing lines. Faced with brick veneer, the facade is lengthened by the planting beds on either side of the entrance and the wall extension out beyond the garage wing. Satisfying weather protection is afforded at the entrance, and convenient access is available to the garage and basement.

Closet space is abundant, and baths and lavatory are very well located and ample-sized. For the all-around privacy of two stories, plus all the conveniences of contemporary living, this home is ideal for the large or growing family.

AREA: First floor: 1,256 sq. ft.
Second floor: 1,215 sq. ft.

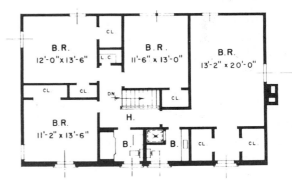

SECOND FLOOR PLAN

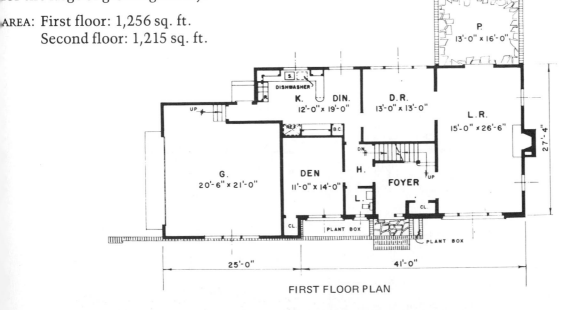

FIRST FLOOR PLAN

The Kirk-Wood

Inside this two-story traditional home are many of the features most requested by those undertaking new home construction, wrapped in a pleasant, highly acceptable colonial exterior of hand-split red cedar shingles and brick veneer.

The sunken family room is separated from the kitchen-dinette by a wrought-iron rail and features a beamed ceiling, stone fireplace, and sliding glass doors.

A gentle stairway leads to the four second floor bedrooms; a master bedroom suite with a room-size walk-in closet, two complete bathrooms, and three additional bedrooms complete the second floor.

AREA: First floor: 1,270 sq. ft.
　　　Second floor: 1,204 sq. ft.
　　　Garage: 517 sq. ft.

SECOND FLOOR PLAN

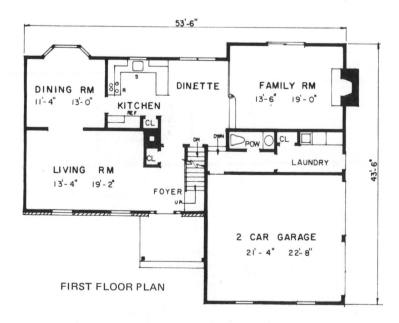

FIRST FLOOR PLAN

The Fair-Lawn

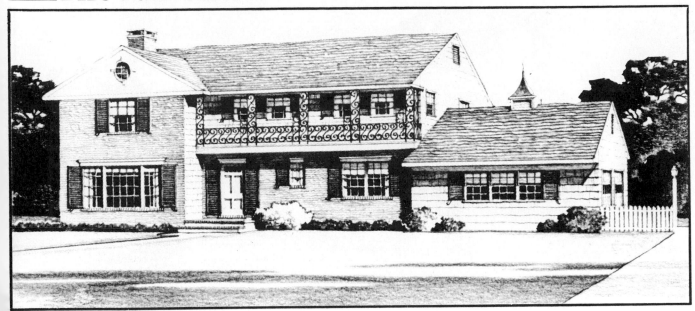

The elegance of a two-story home will always remain, despite the changing trends in home building.

This balconied, eight-room home displays that everlasting Southern charm of wrought-iron and brick with a stately gabled wing on one side and a long roofed garage wing on the other. The finishing touches of cupola, fence, and lamp post complete this picture.

Inside, the planning has evolved into a most modern arrangement of rooms for convenient and gracious living. A multitude of spacious closets, 2½ baths, a delightfully large kitchen, dining room, living room, and den plus four generous bedrooms all combine to suit your mode of living.

AREA: First floor: 1,270 sq. ft. (excluding garage & porch)
Second floor: 1,280 sq. ft.

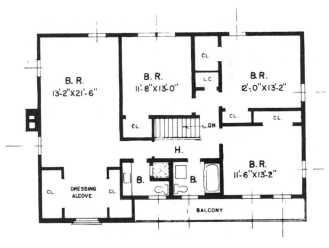

SECOND FLOOR PLAN

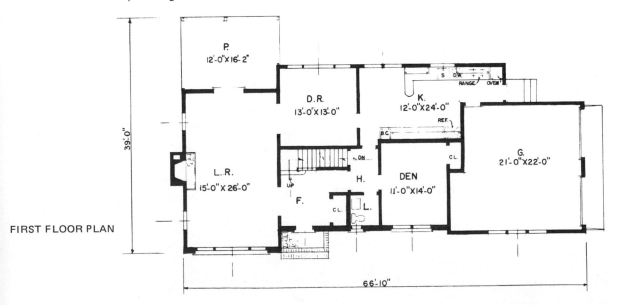

FIRST FLOOR PLAN

The Pem-Brooke

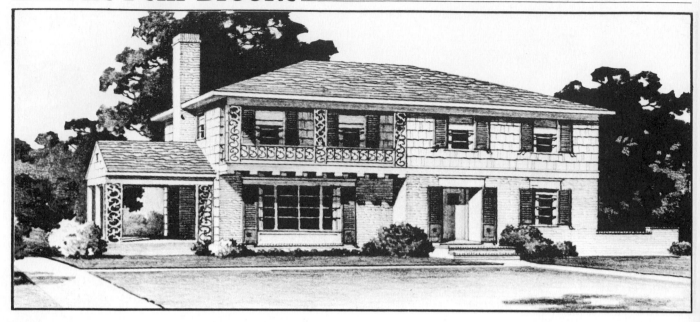

The balcony and wrought-iron porch posts of this gracious colonial exterior give an air of delicate beauty to this home.

The formal mode of living of the old colonials is carried out with modern convenience in this plan. On the first floor the large living room, dining room and step-saving kitchen are enhanced by the addition of a den, well located off the main foyer, as well as a lovely, vanitoried powder room at the entrance vestibule.

The second floor provides four large bedrooms and two full baths plus many ample clothes closets, a linen closet, and a dressing alcove for the master bedroom.

That is not the end, however, for this home built on a sloping lot provides garage and additional living area in the basement, on ground level, consisting of a maid's room and bath, a recreation room, laundry, and combination boiler-work room.

AREA: First floor: 1,300 sq. ft. (excluding porch)
Second floor: 1,300 sq. ft.

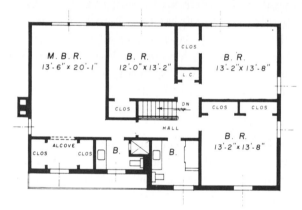

SECOND FLOOR PLAN

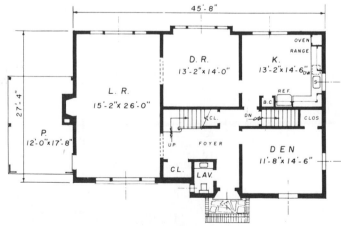

FIRST FLOOR PLAN

The Marquette

The capacity of a 17th century French mansard roof to provide extra space on the second floor is clearly illustrated in this pleasant traditional house. Old World charm emerges from such exterior details as the mansard roof, brick quoins at ends of structure, wood shingles on garage, scalloped, leaded-glass entrance doors and windows, and paneled mouldings.

Inside, to the left of the foyer, is a spacious living room with fireplace and three exposures. The dining room adjoins the living room as well as the kitchen-dinette area with its adjacent, separate-entry laundry. The plan is complemented by the front vestibule lavatory and private study.

On the second floor, four large bedrooms, including a master bedroom with two closets and stall-shower bath, and a centrally located bath serve the needs of any family.

AREA: First floor: 1,364 sq. ft.
Second floor: 1,264 sq. ft.

SECOND FLOOR PLAN

FIRST FLOOR PLAN

The George-Towne

This charming house, with its gabled entrance portico, provides beauty as well as comfort for a large family. The formal foyer separating the living room and dining room leads straight to the large kitchen and family room with its angled fireplace.

On the second floor, the family can find comfort and privacy with four generous bedrooms, two full baths, and nine closets.

AREA: First floor: 1,317 sq. ft.
Second floor: 1,317 sq. ft.

SECOND FLOOR PLAN

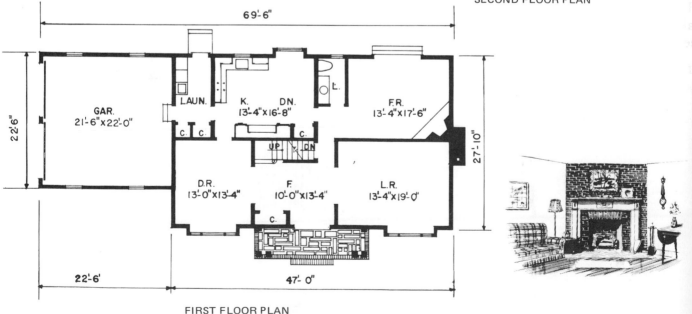

FIRST FLOOR PLAN

The Wood-Mont

Colonial charm could hardly be more appealingly captured than in this history-based design with a horizontal look. Traffic is effectively distributed throughout the first floor and, by means of a wrought-iron staircase, directly to the four second floor bedrooms.

The formal living room and dining room on either side of the foyer are complemented by the easy, relaxed atmosphere of the family room with its fireplace and sliding glass doors. The first floor is rounded out by the kitchen-dinette area with convenient laundry, which has a large closet and entry to garage and backyard.

Upstairs, four spacious bedrooms, three with walk-in closets, and two full baths provide for the needs of the family.

AREA: First floor: 1,340 sq. ft.
Second floor: 1,315 sq. ft.

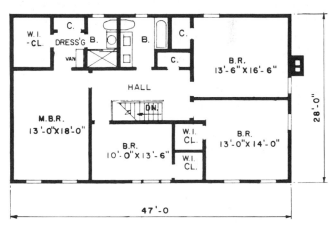

SECOND FLOOR PLAN

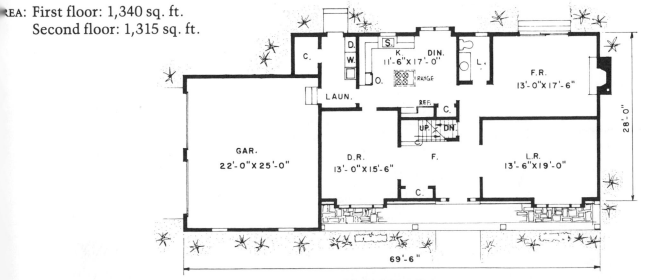

FIRST FLOOR PLAN

61

The Stone-Haven

This interesting Dutch colonial design features the space-creating gambrel roof for the particular purpose of sheltering the bedrooms on the second floor without sacrificing floor space.

The sunken living room has three exposures, with a colonial brick fireplace and wrought-iron railings producing a balcony effect to the dining room. An optional additional room on the second floor can be used as a den, sewing room, or fifth bedroom.

The traditional flavor of the exterior is accentuated by the symmetry of the windows, massive centered chimney, hand-split red cedar shingles, gabled dormers, and shuttered, multi-paned windows.

AREA: First floor: 1,514 sq. ft.
Second floor: 1,188 sq. ft.

SECOND FLOOR PLAN

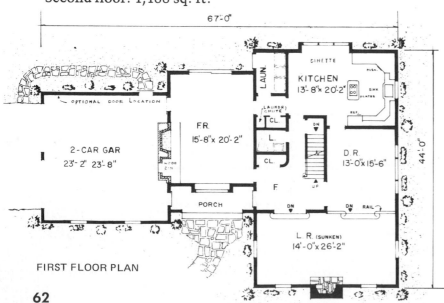

FIRST FLOOR PLAN

The Somerset

The traditional appearance of this Southern colonial, with its large portico and square columns, relects the comfort and elegance built within and makes it right at home in the city, suburb, or country.

The air of gracious living is immediately apparent as one moves under the entrance portico, which shelters the front entrance door. What better welcoming sight than a large foyer with a sweeping, grand, circular staircase? This is the key to efficient traffic distribution throughout the first floor areas and to the second floor. The open, spacious stairwell, with its wrought-iron ornamental handrailing, eliminates any feeling of congestion on the second floor.

This is a house which makes optimum use of every square foot of space and has traditional old-fashioned enchantment, charm, and dignity.

AREA: First floor: 1,525 sq. ft.
Second floor: 1,185 sq. ft.
Basement: 1,525 sq. ft.
Garage: 630 sq. ft.

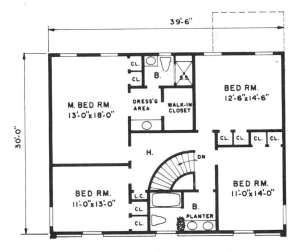

SECOND FLOOR PLAN

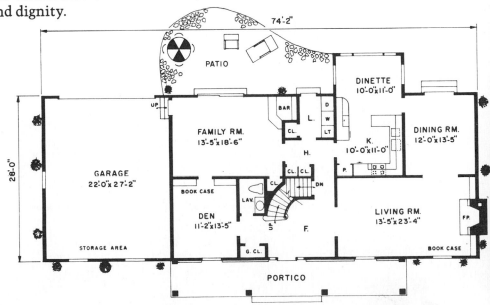

FIRST FLOOR PLAN

The Bel-More

This design offers a variation from the standard two-story design. To the right of the foyer is a private bedroom with adjacent bath. Across the foyer is a spacious den.

The living-dining room forms a large open area across the rear of the house. Just a few steps from the well-organized kitchen-dinette area is a laundry room with entry to the garage.

Upstairs, three comfortable bedrooms with generous closets and two bathrooms complete this extremely livable plan.

AREA: First floor: 1,720 sq. ft.
　　　Second floor: 785 sq. ft.

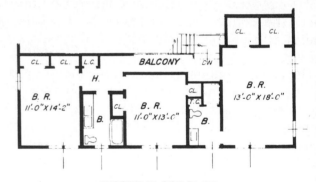

SECOND FLOOR PLAN

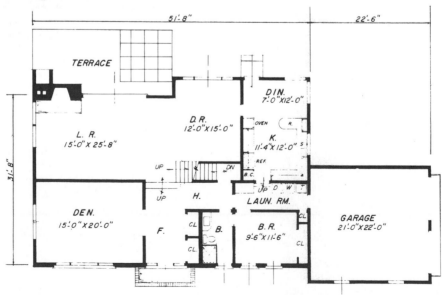

FIRST FLOOR PLAN

The Devonshire

There is no doubt that the romance of English Tudor architecture is captured in the exterior styling of this two-story, four-bedroom plan, which should delight families with a taste for continental design; the diamond-shaped, leaded windows, half-timber, and stucco evoke memories of the past, but the floor plan is strictly contemporary.

The front entrance is sheltered by the gabled overhang, which leads into an impressive entry which welcomes guests and provides a handsome view of the fireplace in the beamed-ceiling family room on the left and living room on the right.

On the second floor, the family will find relaxation and comfort. The master bedroom, with its three closets, one a walk-in, built-in vanity, and stall-shower bath will satisfy even the most demanding family. The other three large bedrooms are well served by a central, compartmented bath.

AREA: First floor: 1,333 sq. ft.
Second floor: 1,333 sq. ft.

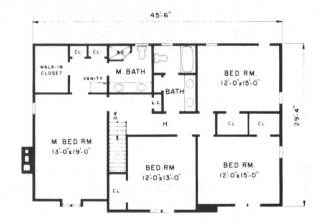

SECOND FLOOR PLAN

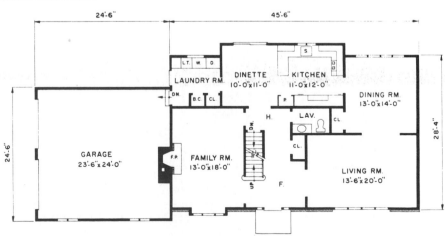

FIRST FLOOR PLAN

The Stone-Ridge

The contemporary exterior styling of this two-story home is equalled only by the up-to-date living comfort on the inside.

The floor plan features a large, private family room with access to a two-car garage. A formal entrance foyer with flagstone flooring separates a huge living room with fireplace from a spacious dining room. A compact, U-shaped kitchen, dinette, pantry, and lavatory complete the first floor.

A full complement of four bedrooms, two baths, and seven closets, one a walk-in, make up the sleeping level on the second floor.

AREA: First floor: 1,440 sq. ft.
Second floor: 1,230 sq. ft.

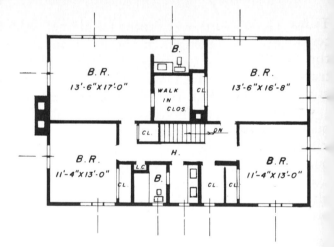

SECOND FLOOR PLAN

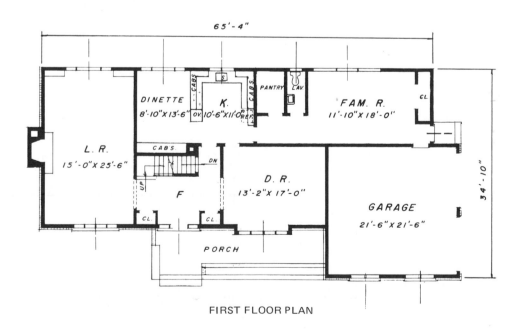

FIRST FLOOR PLAN

The Churchill

Timbers, stucco, and a variety of roof lines add interest to this English Tudor-inspired, two-story, three-bedroom design. The recessed double-door entrance leads to a spacious foyer which easily radiates traffic to all the rooms on the first floor.

A massive brick-faced fireplace is featured in the beamed-ceiling family room, which is open to the kitchen-dinette and is accessible to a screened porch.

Upstairs, the lavish master bedroom suite includes two closets, one a room-size walk-in, and a private bath with Roman whirlpool bathtub.

AREA: First floor: 1,695 sq. ft.
Second floor: 1,085 sq. ft.
Garage: 580 sq. ft.
Basement: 1,648 sq. ft.

SECOND FLOOR PLAN

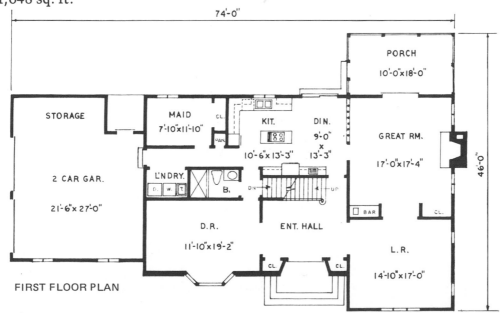

FIRST FLOOR PLAN

The Old-Field

Styles in houses may come and go, but for enduring popularity, it is hard to beat the familiar two-story colonial.

Inside, the large and impressive foyer makes a fine reception area, leading on the left to the formal dining room or on the right to the spacious living room with fireplace. The first floor is completed by a recreation room with optional fireplace, kitchen-dinette area, laundry, lavatory, and maid's room.

On the second floor, the family will find comfort and privacy. The master bedroom has a dressing room, five closets, and stall-shower bath. The other three bedrooms are well served by a large bath and a total of eight closets.

AREA: First floor: 1,610 sq. ft.
Second floor: 1,192 sq. ft.

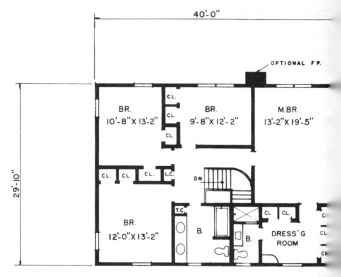

SECOND FLOOR PLAN

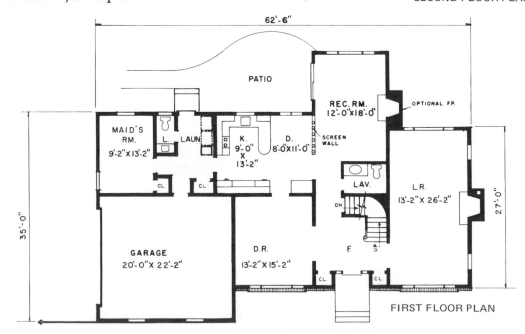

FIRST FLOOR PLAN

The Nottingham

This four-bedroom, two-story, full-basement design has all the traditional elements of the English Tudor manor house. Basic characteristics include a massive brick chimney with protruding chimney pots, steep roofs of varying heights, an angular bay window, narrow diamond-paned windows with leaded glass, and half-timber on stucco walls.

An open staircase leads directly from the entrance foyer to the sleeping area, and the wide upstairs hall features a balcony with ornamental wood rail overlooking the cathedral-ceiling living room below.

The four comfortable bedrooms are highlighted by the luxurious master bedroom, which includes a lounge with built-in bookcases, walk-in closet, and stall-shower bath. The three remaining bedrooms are complemented by a spacious, compartmented bath and eight closets, one a walk-in.

AREA: First floor: 1,388 sq. ft.
Second floor: 1,446 sq. ft.

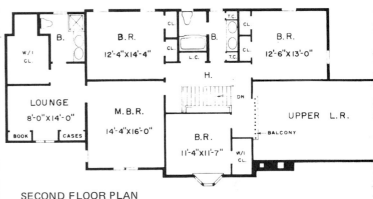

SECOND FLOOR PLAN

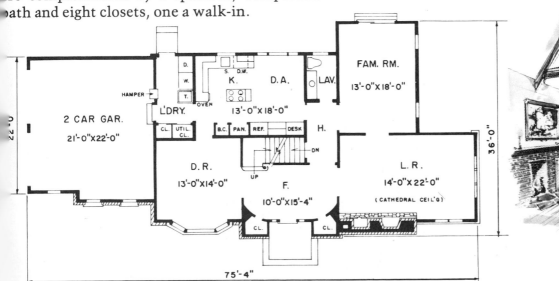

FIRST FLOOR PLAN

The Chateau-Gaye

This chateau design is derived from native French architecture; it has the appeal of simple elegance combined with a tasteful use of ornamental detailing. The combination of red cedar shingles, brick veneer, diamond-paned windows over the recessed entrance, and the steep, hipped roof will remain in style indefinitely.

The impressive reception foyer distributes traffic effectively throughout the first floor and, by a curved open stairway, to the master bedroom suite with its lounge, and the additional three bedrooms.

Sliding glass doors in the family room, which features a brick fireplace and a built-in refreshment bar, take full advantage of the rear patio, lounging, and garden areas.

AREA: First floor: 1,650 sq. ft.
Second floor: 1,525 sq. ft.

SECOND FLOOR PLAN

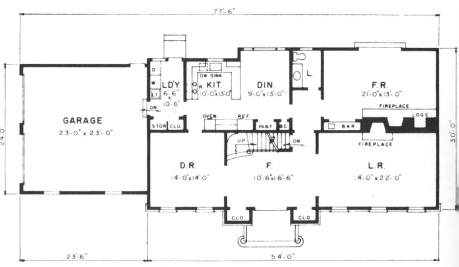

FIRST FLOOR PLAN

The Drift-Wood

All the regal luxury of the traditional two-story home is contained in the colonial styling of this large, nine-room plan. The front of this home presents long, low-appearing lines. Faced with stone veneer, the facade is lengthened by the planting beds on either side of the entrance.

Inside, the formal dining room and living room with fireplace are complemented by the cozy den and step-saving kitchen.

Upstairs, five comfortable bedrooms, two bathrooms, and ten closets meet the needs of the large family.

AREA: First floor: 1,325 sq. ft.
Second floor: 1,600 sq. ft.

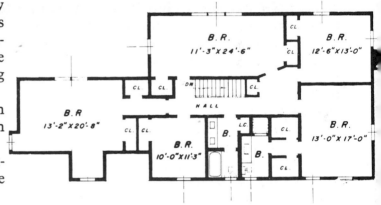

SECOND FLOOR PLAN

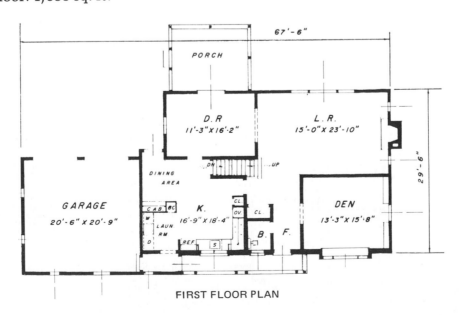

FIRST FLOOR PLAN

The Wimbledon

Once again, English architecture is enjoying wide popularity because there is something about the dark, hand-hewn timber and stone exterior, the many-paned and diamond-shaped windows, and the overall look of solidarity of this style which gives an impression of enduring comfort and happiness. Typical is the open staircase which leads directly from the entrance foyer to the four bedrooms and open balcony on the second floor.

A decorative metal circular staircase provides ready access to the upper "balcony library," which is located at the end of the living room, while directly behind is the beamed-ceiling family room.

The family can find privacy and relaxation in the four bedrooms and two baths on the second floor. Highlighting the sleeping area is the master bedroom with lounge, built-in vanity, walk-in closet, and stall-shower bath.

AREA: First floor: 1,450 sq. ft.
Second floor: 1,500 sq. ft.
Basement: 1,200 sq. ft.
Garage: 560 sq. ft.

SECOND FLOOR PLAN

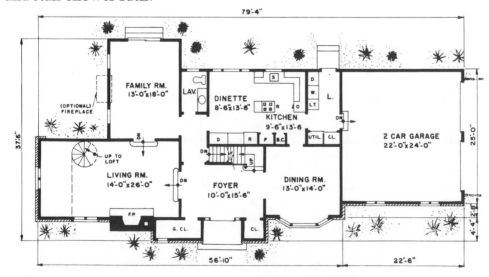

FIRST FLOOR PLAN

The Berkshire

The glamour and serenity of French Provincial styling are on display throughout this unusual 1½ story design and make this the perfect home for the family with a well-developed feeling for traditional influence. The main interior features are the grand foyer with its circular staircase, the sunken living room flanked by wrought-iron rails and grilles, and the built-in wet bar and fireplace with French mantel in the family room. Accessible to rear sundeck are the family room and the well-equipped island kitchen.

The first floor master bedroom suite has two closets, one a room-size walk-in, dressing area vanity with full-length mirror, and a complete bath with double-basin vanity, sunken Roman tub, glass-enclosed shower, and sauna.

The second floor is made up of two additional bedrooms, a central bath, and generous closet space.

AREA: First floor: 2,497 sq. ft.
Second floor: 527 sq. ft.
Garage: 550 sq. ft.

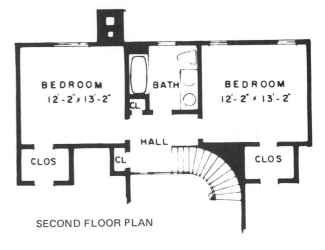

SECOND FLOOR PLAN

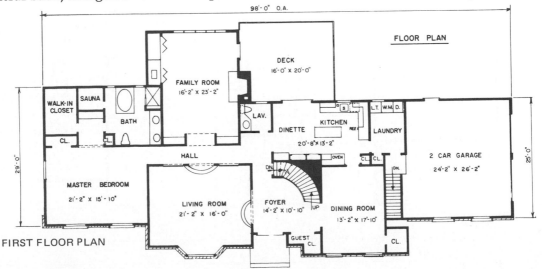

FIRST FLOOR PLAN

The Hawthorne

The impressive facade of this traditional design is achieved by the colonial details of its one-story, columned portico, hand-split red cedar shingles, small-paned windows, and the formal balance of the three second floor dormers and the first floor bay windows.

Inside, the grand foyer is the key to efficient traffic circulation. Special features include a sunken living room; family room with fireplace, wet bar, and sliding glass doors to rear patio; island kitchen; private bedroom suite with five closets, and complete bath with tub, stall shower, and vanity; and two-car garage with closed-off storage area.

Three bedrooms and two baths complete the second floor.

AREA: First floor: 2,396 sq. ft.
Second floor: 637 sq. ft.
Garage: 616 sq. ft.

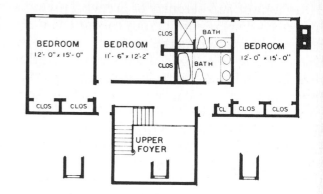

SECOND FLOOR PLAN

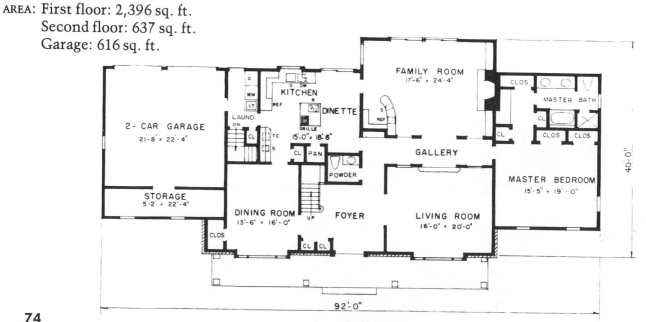

FIRST FLOOR PLAN

The East-Windsor

The colonial dignity of the exterior of this stately, two-story home continues throughout the planning of the interior. Spaciousness is a keynote here and is apparent from the room sizes indicated.

The service area here is a family's dream. Separate dining and food preparation areas highlight the kitchen; a large utility room has ample space for freezer, washer, dryer, and counters. A service lavatory and separate stair to the maid's room and bath located over the garage complete the first floor.

Four large bedrooms, with walk-in and sliding door closets, plus two full baths make up the second floor sleeping area of this home.

AREA: First floor: 1,627 sq. ft. (excluding garage & porch)
Second floor: 1,510 sq. ft.

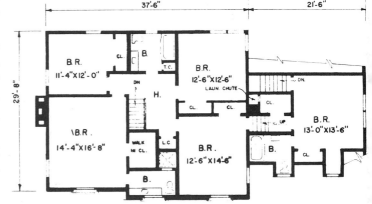

SECOND FLOOR PLAN

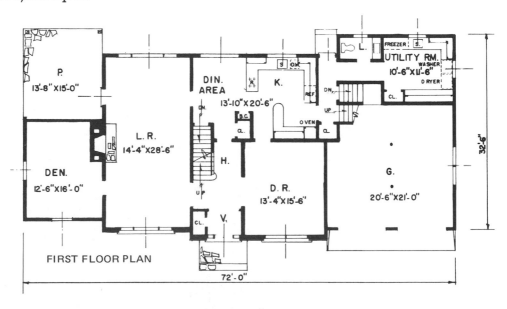

FIRST FLOOR PLAN

75

The Heritage

The formal appearance of this two-story, symmetrical colonial design is softened by the addition of the barn-type, two-car garage at one side and more than equalled in the spacious, well-ordered interior room arrangement. The grand entrance foyer provides excellent circulation throughout the entire house, and of special interest are the twin fireplaces, one each in living and family rooms.

For those with a yen for luxury, the second floor master bedroom suite offers two walk-in closets, a tub and stall-shower bath, vanity in dressing area, and a private sundeck. A compartmented bath with twin basins and full-wall mirrored vanity services the other three bedrooms.

AREA: First floor: 1,680 sq. ft.
Second floor: 1,473 sq. ft.
Garage: 575 sq. ft.

SECOND FLOOR PLAN

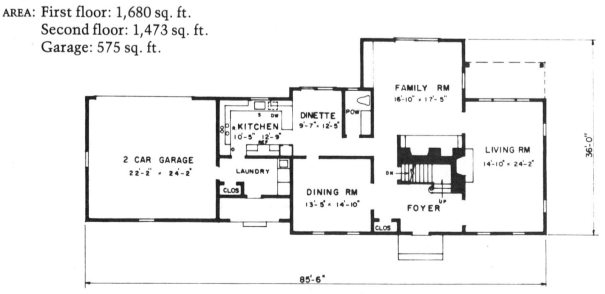

FIRST FLOOR PLAN

The Cortland

The drama of high, sloped ceilings makes this five-bedroom contemporary home something special. The living room and family room, which feature a "see-through" fireplace, have beamed ceilings which soar to the height of the roofline, echoing the intriguing "slant" of the imposing exterior.

Two first floor bedrooms and bath are separated from the living areas for peace and quiet. Three additional bedrooms and bath off the second floor balcony, which overlooks the family room and living room below, may be finished at a later date, if so desired.

An interesting feature is the rear L-shaped wood deck which is serviced by the sliding glass doors of the dinette, living room, and family room.

AREA: First floor: 2,302 sq. ft.
Second floor: 888 sq. ft.
Sundeck: 472 sq. ft.
Garage: 719 sq. ft.

SECOND FLOOR PLAN

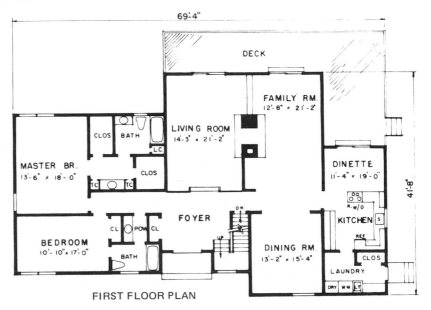

FIRST FLOOR PLAN

The Cedar-Brook

For the comfort-loving modern family, here is a handsome choice which cherishes the heritage of its earlier ancestors. The colonial paneled door opens to the large foyer, with sliding-door coat closet and attractive stairway with wrought-iron railing. Immediately to the right is the living room, with an informal family room at the rear with fireplace and sliding glass doors to the terrace.

The kitchen-dinette is a true family center. Off the kitchen are the laundry with its service entrance and a two-car garage.

On the second floor are five lovely bedrooms with ample closets and two modern luxurious baths. One is in the master bedroom off a dressing area with a walk-in closet and built-in vanity. A centrally located powder room off the foyer serves the first floor, and the stairway to the full basement is also in this central location for convenience.

AREA: First floor: 1,720 sq. ft.
Second floor: 1,720 sq. ft.
Garage: 700 sq. ft.

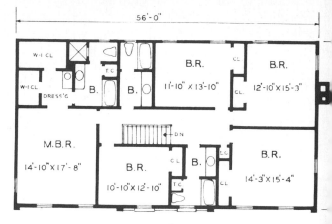

SECOND FLOOR PLAN

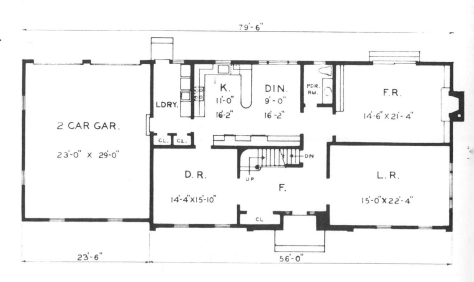

FIRST FLOOR PLAN

78

The Fair-Oaks

Although the day of French nobility is gone, French Provincial styling is gaining renewed popularity in America; this two-story, four-bedroom model is a good example.

The imposing exterior is complete with steep hipped roof, charming window detailing which includes half-dormered windows, brick veneer with brick quoins at the corners, massive chimney, double front entrance doors, and a decorative cupola on the roof of the garage wing.

Inside, the foyer allows access to the dining room, living room, family room, or kitchen-dinette area without cross-room circulation. Completing the first floor are a lavatory, laundry, and maid's room with full bath.

On the second floor, there are four spacious bedrooms and two baths. The master bedroom has a dressing area, a stall-shower bath, and two over-sized closets. The other three bedrooms are well-served by a double-sink, compartmented bath and ten closets.

AREA: First floor: 1,854 sq. ft.
Second floor: 1,596 sq. ft.
Garage: 485 sq. ft.

SECOND FLOOR PLAN

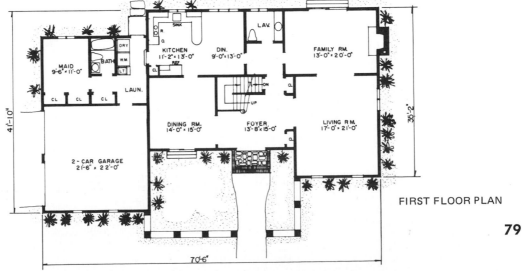

FIRST FLOOR PLAN

The Wellington

This impressive exterior, with its stone veneer, half-timber, stucco, bays, half-dormers, and diamond-paned windows, is distinctively English Tudor. Visual variety, so pleasing outside, is continued indoors as well.

The grand foyer forms the primary entrance and directs traffic into all parts of the house. Straight ahead the 17' by 23' living room, with its cathedral ceiling, features a massive brick "see-through" fireplace and leads into the dining and family rooms. The kitchen-dinette is amply supplied with base and wall cabinets, appliances, etc., and is equipped with an "island" range.

The lavish, private master bedroom suite on the first floor is accessible through a lounge; it has three closets, one a walk-in, dressing room vanity, and complete bath with glass-enclosed stall shower. Three large bedrooms, two baths, and a lounge or hobby room complete the second floor.

AREA: First floor: 2,310 sq. ft.
Second floor: 1,146 sq. ft.
Sundeck: 141 sq. ft.
Garage: 644 sq. ft.

SECOND FLOOR PLAN

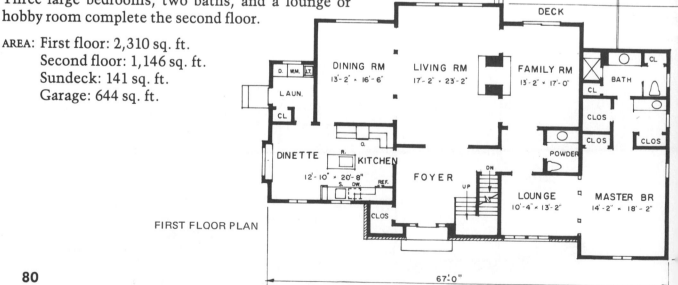

FIRST FLOOR PLAN

The Chateau-Blanc

Visions of royal living come quickly to mind in looking at this elegant French Provincial two-story, four-bedroom design. There's royal living inside too, with spaciousness the keynote; the foyer is room-size with a sweeping, curved staircase to the second floor; the kitchen features a dinette with a rectangular bay window, and the sunken family room at the rear is serviced by the raised entrance foyer level.

The multi-paned exterior French doors of the living and dining rooms open into the front balustrated courtyard.

A service stair to the basement from the two-car garage provides additional storage area, and extensive use of brick veneer helps to minimize maintenance requirements.

On the second floor, the master bedroom suite features two closets, one a walk-in, and a complete bathroom with a full-length mirrored vanity; two other bedrooms share a lavish bath, and the fourth bedroom has a private bath.

AREA: First floor: 1,840 sq. ft.
Second floor: 1,640 sq. ft.
Garage: 650 sq. ft.

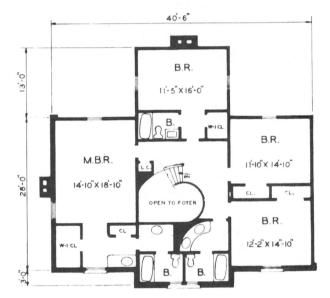

SECOND FLOOR PLAN

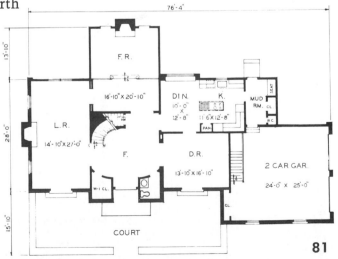

FIRST FLOOR PLAN

The San Mateo

Many details typical of the Southwest Spanish architecture are included in this two-story, four-bedroom house: stucco, brick veneer, arched and vertical windows, cantilevered balconies, and hand-carved wood double-entrance doors. To the right of the entrance "room-size" foyer is the living room, and behind it is the sunken family room with wood-beamed ceiling and a rubblestone wood-burning fireplace. Laundry facilities are located next to the kitchen-dinette and adjacent to the maid's room and the double garage. A powder room is conveniently located just off the foyer.

The second floor is reached by the impressive curved staircase. The master suite has two closets, one a "room-size" walk-in, sitting area, open balcony, and a luxurious bath with twin-basin vanity, stall shower, and Roman whirlpool bathtub. Two complete bathrooms service the other three bedrooms.

AREA: First floor: 1,940 sq. ft.
Second floor: 1,620 sq. ft.
Garage: 620 sq. ft.

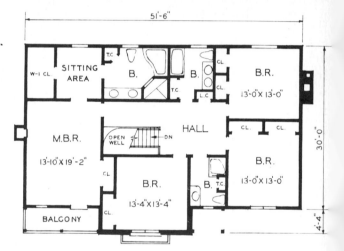

SECOND FLOOR PLAN

FIRST FLOOR PLAN

The East-Brooke

There is no doubt that the romance of the traditional French Provincial countryside exterior styling of this two-story, four-bedroom plan should delight families with a taste for continental design. Its eye-catching character is derived from the curved window heads, angular bays, brick quoins at all corners of the brick veneer, steep roofs, and the diamond-paned, copper-roofed picture bay over the double-door recessed entrance.

The circular staircase with wrought-iron railing provides a luxurious access to the four bedrooms on the second floor which complete a plan which retains all the good living qualities and hospitality of an earlier era.

AREA: First floor: 1,900 sq. ft.
Second floor: 1,692 sq. ft.
Garage: 576 sq. ft.
Basement: 1,725 sq. ft.

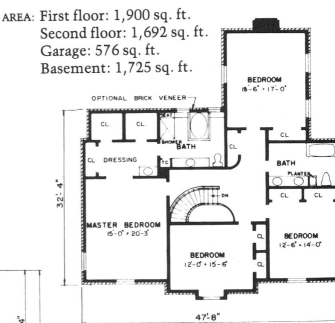

SECOND FLOOR PLAN

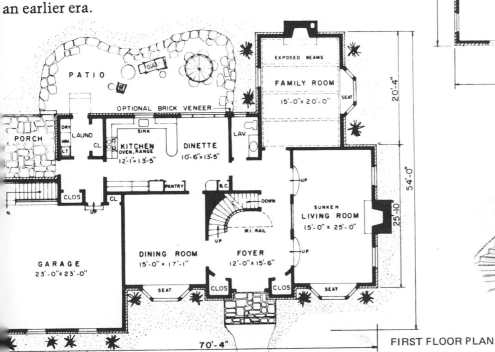

FIRST FLOOR PLAN

83

The Buena-Vista

20th century living at its most luxurious is possible in this unusual contemporary two-story design. The exterior is vertical V-joint redwood, asphalt shingle roof, and casement and transomed windows.

Inside, to the rear is the dropped "great room" with its fireplace, full glass walls, and sliding doors which open to the L-shaped wood deck. The U-shaped "cathedral ceiling" kitchen is a delight, and, for informal meals, there is the dinette, which has access to the rear deck.

To the right of the foyer is the bedroom area, highlighted by the master bedroom suite with its own private balcony, two walk-in closets, stall-shower and tub bathroom. The other bedroom has a compartmented "powder room-bathroom."

Upstairs, the open foyer looks down on the "great room," and the two bedrooms and study are serviced by a common bath.

AREA: First floor: 2,560 sq. ft.
Second floor: 1,130 sq. ft.
Garage: 570 sq. ft.

SECOND FLOOR PLAN

FIRST FLOOR PLAN

The South-Hampton

Elegance is the keynote of this two-story, English Tudor home. Projecting bay and dormer windows, half-timber decorative work, smooth stucco, diamond-paned windows, and large chimney are authentic period details.

The angular dinette, which opens to the rear deck, is the dramatic highlight of the kitchen-dinette area. The "cathedral ceiling" family room with brick fireplace also leads to the open deck. A laundry room, pantry, lavatory, powder room, and a two-car garage with a room-size storage area complete the first floor.

Upstairs, the second floor contains a total of five bedrooms. The master suite is serviced by a private bath consisting of a twin-basin vanity, stall shower, two walk-in closets, and dressing area. The other four bedrooms are convenient to the compartmented bath. An open balcony overlooks the family room below.

AREA: First floor: 2,120 sq. ft.
Second floor: 1,950 sq. ft.
Garage: 660 sq. ft.

SECOND FLOOR PLAN

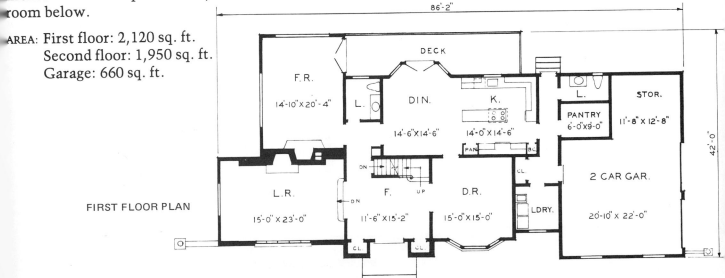

FIRST FLOOR PLAN

The North Hampton

English Tudor homes are among the most favored in America today. The varied roof lines, distinctive materials such as brick and half-timber, and the unique architectural treatment of diamond-paned windows, massive chimney, double-entrance oak doors, and half dormers contribute to the popularity.

To the left of the foyer is the 1½ story beamed-ceiling living room which features a balcony library at the end of the room, accessible by a dramatic, spiral, wrought-iron stair.

The main circular stairs lead to the four bedrooms on the second floor. On the right is the master bedroom suite, which includes a dressing area with two room-size closets, a private lounge, and a luxury bath with Roman whirlpool tub. The other three bedrooms are serviced by a compartmented main bath.

AREA: First floor: 2,218 sq. ft.
Second floor: 2,200 sq. ft.
Garage: 644 sq. ft.
Basement: 1,855 sq. ft.

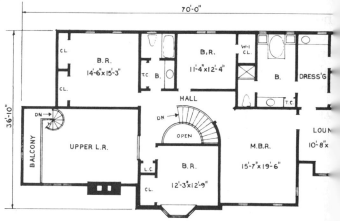

SECOND FLOOR PLAN

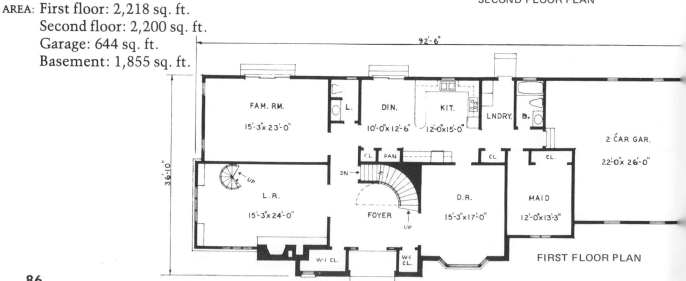

FIRST FLOOR PLAN

The Cornell

A pleasant combination of the old and the new is expressed in this home's warmth of feeling on the exterior and its convenience of planning inside.

As the entrance hall extends to the rear of the house, it provides convenient passage to the living room, kitchen, basement, bedrooms, and bath, respectively. The living room features a full-size fireplace, lots of floor space, and entry to a handy breezeway.

AREA: First floor: 1,186 sq. ft.
Second floor: 600 sq. ft.

SECOND FLOOR PLAN

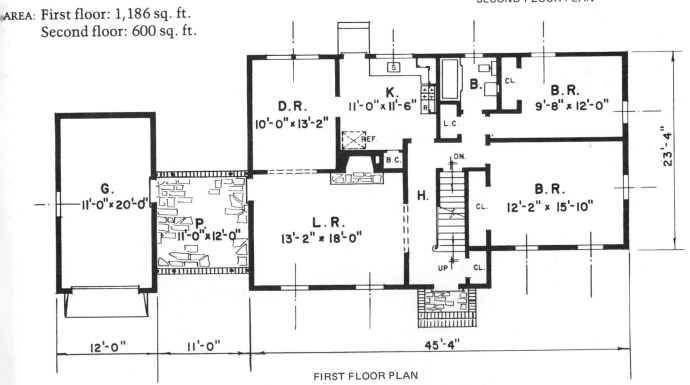

FIRST FLOOR PLAN

The Nantucket

This long, low dwelling appears to be a conventional ranch, but it has room for two future bedrooms and a bath on the second floor.

The living room has a large picture window set in a box bay; beyond the living room is the dining room. The family room, kitchen, and laundry room are all in a line across the rear of the house.

A hall leads to the privacy of three bedrooms and two baths, completing the first floor.

AREA: First floor: 1,772 sq. ft.
Second floor: 483 sq. ft.

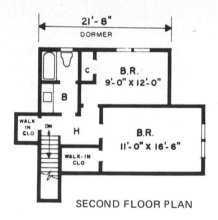

SECOND FLOOR PLAN

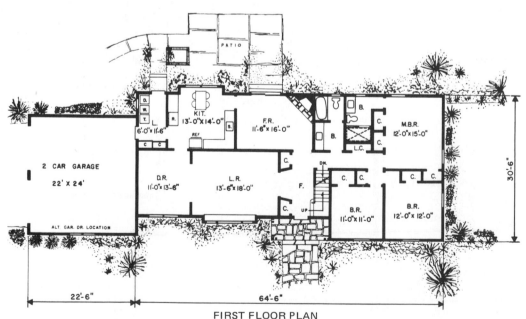

FIRST FLOOR PLAN

The Vancouver

Entrance to this lovely home is through a garden court, and the double-door entry leads straight ahead to the spacious living room. The kitchen-dinette makes meal preparation easy; adjacent to it is the paneled family room, which features a raised-hearth fireplace and sliding glass doors to the rear patio.

The three bedrooms are of modest size, but the master bedroom has its own private stall-shower bath. Two additional bedrooms and bath can be built on the second floor if needed at a later date.

AREA: First floor: 2,300 sq. ft.
Second floor: 493 sq. ft.

The Ponderosa

The entrance courtyard, with its warmth and charm, is a familiar detail of Spanish architecture. Once past the wrought-iron gate, the visitor is greeted by the waffle-patterned entrance door. Inside, a palatial, two-story, circular foyer leads to the two bedrooms on the second floor.

On the first floor, the "see-through" fireplace is the focal point of the beamed-ceiling family room and the living room. The efficient kitchen has a cooking island, and the three bedrooms, served by two full bathrooms, are secluded at one side of the house.

AREA: First floor: 3,090 sq. ft.
Second floor: 676 sq. ft.
Garage: 552 sq. ft.

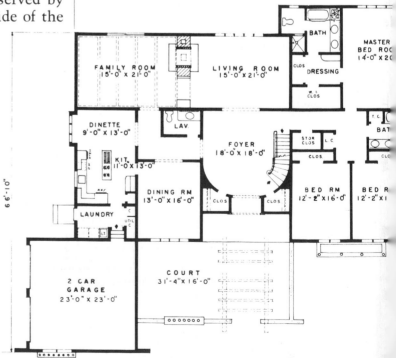

FIRST FLOOR PLAN

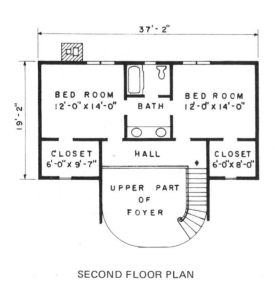

SECOND FLOOR PLAN

The Yarborough

The covered front portico, brick veneer, wood shingles, board and batten vertical siding, and shuttered windows give this 1½ story house a feeling of timeless beauty.

Inside, the family will find relaxation in the spacious living areas. Two bedrooms complete the first floor plan; the master bedroom suite features a fireplace, walk-in closets, and compartmented bath.

Three additional bedrooms and two full baths on the second floor may be finished at a later date, if so desired.

AREA: First floor: 2,800 sq. ft.
Second floor: 1,130 sq. ft.

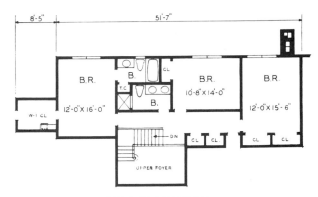

SECOND FLOOR PLAN

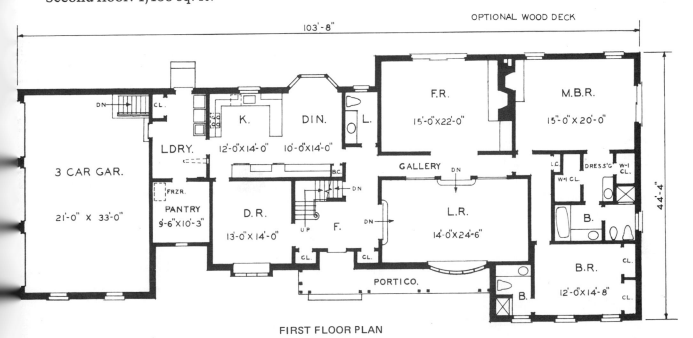

FIRST FLOOR PLAN

The Wilshire

To the right of the spacious foyer is the sunken living room, and to the rear is the paneled family room with a fireplace and triple sliding glass door. The U-shaped kitchen/dinette with sliding glass door is a delight. A spare room off the laundry and two-car garage may be used as a maid's quarters or hobby room.

Two bedrooms, each with its own private bath, complete the first floor. Upstairs, the two bedrooms and bath can be finished at a later date, if so desired.

AREA: First floor: 2,290 sq. ft.
Second floor: 630 sq. ft.

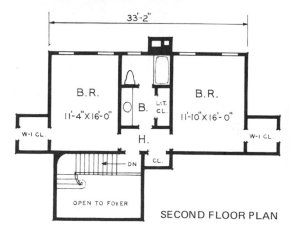

SECOND FLOOR PLAN

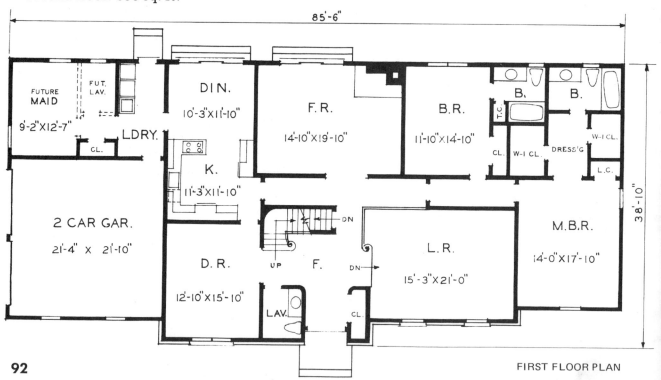

FIRST FLOOR PLAN

SPLIT-LEVEL AND MULTI-LEVEL

Split-levels feature three or four levels. This type offers separation of living and bedroom areas, as in a two-story house, but the flights of stairs are shorter. Split-levels are especially suitable for rolling terrain. More land is required than for a two-story, but more livable space is possible on the same land than in a ranch.

Multi-levels are sometimes called by other names, such as raised ranch or bi-level. In this type of house, the front foyer is at ground level, with a stairway up to the main living area and another down to what would ordinarily be the basement. Because the basement is raised out of the ground enough to permit windows above ground, the area is utilized for living purposes and usually contains a recreation or informal room.

The Lombardy

The attractive exterior of this three-bedroom, split-level house promises comfortable family living. Inside, we find warm, welcoming rooms efficiently arranged to suit any family's needs.

AREA: First & Second levels: 1,400 sq. ft.

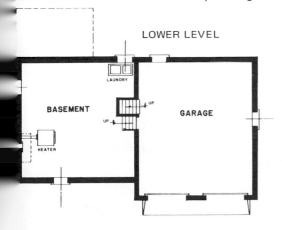

LOWER LEVEL

LAUNDRY

BASEMENT   UP   GARAGE

UP

HEATER

P.
10'-0"x 16'-0"

D. R.
11'-0"x11'-2"

K.
11'-2"x12'-6"

B.   B.

B. R.
12'-0"x15'-6"

LC

DN   UP   C

25'-10"   UP   H.

L. R.
13'-2"x21'-8"   C

C   B. R.
9'-6"x13'-8"   C   C

B. R.
10'-6"x14'-6"

50'-0"

FIRST AND SECOND LEVELS

The Kimberly

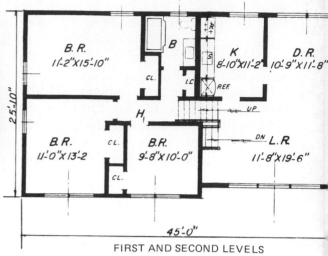

FIRST AND SECOND LEVELS

Modern planning for convenient and comfortable living is to be found in this contemporary design.

The living and dining rooms form a spacious, open area which is highlighted by a fireplace and large, bright windows at each end. A step-saving kitchen is just a few steps away.

Three roomy bedrooms and a full bath round out the upper levels. A garage, lavatory, and cozy den are to be found on the entrance level.

AREA: First & Second levels: 1,110 sq. ft.
　　　Lower level: 300 sq. ft.

LOWER LEVEL

The Hemingway

FIRST AND SECOND LEV

ENTRANCE & LOWER LE

For a narrow lot, this is the ideal split-level plan. Incorporated in only 1,116 sq. ft. are six spacious rooms and a bath. In addition, on the lower level, there is a separate entrance foyer leading to a recreation room, which opens to the rear patio through a sliding glass wall. A laundry room and separate lavatory plus an ample-sized garage complete this level.

Below in the basement, there is a tremendous area which may be put to multi-use as an additional play room, workshop, or hobby area.

AREA: First & second levels: 1,116 sq. ft.
　　　Entrance & lower level: 305 sq. ft.

The Saxony

The secluded sleeping level, located only five steps up from the living area, has three roomy bedrooms and a full bath.

The large, open "L" shape of the living and dining areas gives the appearance of extra size to each area. The kitchen is a wonder of efficiency; brightly lighted by an over-sized window, it has plenty of space for a built-in snack bar in its own corner.

As in most split-level designs, the garage is only a few steps down from the kitchen. Located on the same level is an enormous area which could be finished off with a prefab fireplace for a recreation room. This plan also has a full basement under the living, dining, and kitchen areas.

AREA: First & Second levels: 1,190 sq. ft.
Lower level (future recreation room)
275 sq. ft.

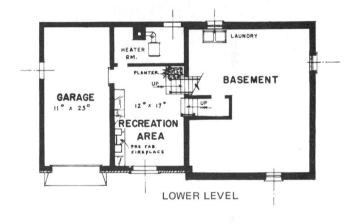

LOWER LEVEL

GARAGE 11° x 23°
HEATER RM.
PLANTER
UP
12° x 17°
RECREATION AREA
PRE FAB FIREPLACE
UP
LAUNDRY
BASEMENT

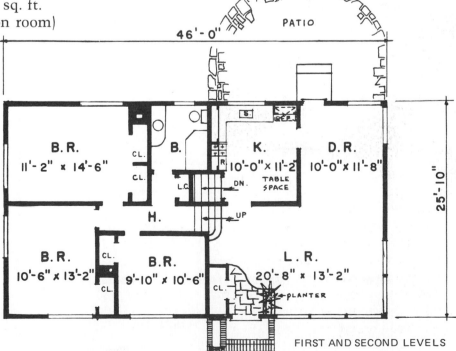

FIRST AND SECOND LEVELS

46'-0"
25'-10"
PATIO

B.R. 11'-2" x 14'-6"
CL.
CL.
B.
K. 10'-0" x 11'-2"
TABLE SPACE
D.R. 10'-0" x 11'-8"
L.C.
DN.
H.
UP
B.R. 10'-6" x 13'-2"
CL.
CL.
B.R. 9'-10" x 10'-6"
CL.
L.R. 20'-8" x 13'-2"
PLANTER
DN.

The Parkway

Split-levels are very popular today, because they can be adapted to different lots. This charming brick and clapboard version is extremely flexible, adaptable to a flat lot as well as one with a slope.

Here you have a wide open plan for living-dining service, enhanced by a brick fireplace wall in the living room and open through the dining room to the airy porch with an adjoining terrace. Only six steps lead up to the private bedroom area.

A full-size, two-car garage is only half a flight down. There is also a combination laundry-lavatory situated on this garage level, while in the basement proper is ample room for a large recreation area.

AREA: First & Second levels: 1,170 sq. ft.
Lower level: 340 sq. ft.

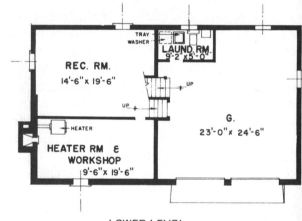

LOWER LEVEL

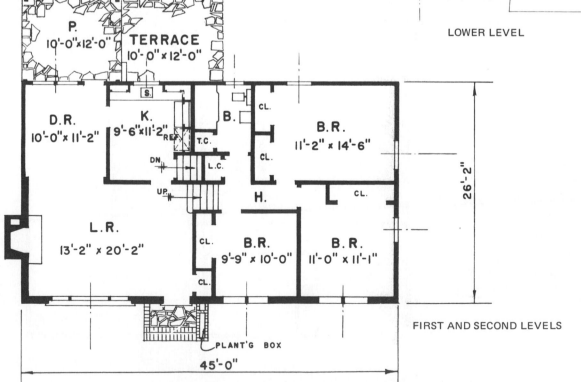

FIRST AND SECOND LEVELS

The Sterling

There is no doubt that a split-level house offers considerable extra space at a minimum of building cost, and although the living, bedroom, and recreation rooms are on different levels, the low number of steps between levels does away with a lot of stair climbing at a single time.

The first thing that one notices in this three-bedroom, split-level is the interesting effect created by the sweeping rooflines and the transomed window treatment in a pleasant vertical style, intermixed with brick veneer and vertical siding.

For those who can orient themselves to split-level living, this carefully planned design, with a long list of features to recommend it, offers visual satisfaction and comfortable living for everyone.

AREA: Upper levels: 1,278 sq. ft.
Lower level: 288 sq. ft.
Basement: 628 sq. ft.
Garage: 262 sq. ft.
Deck: 252 sq. ft.

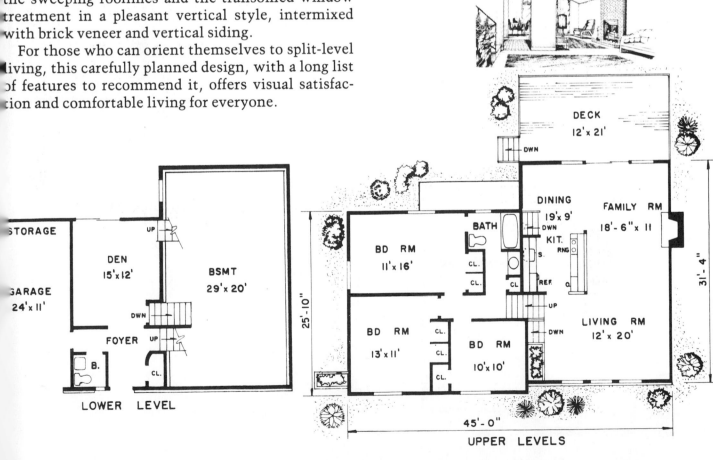

STORAGE

DEN
15'x12'

BSMT
29'x20'

GARAGE
24'x11'

DWN

FOYER   UP

CL.

B.

LOWER LEVEL

DECK
12'x21'

DWN

DINING
19'x9'

BATH

DWN

KIT.
RNG

FAMILY RM
18'-6"x11

BD RM
11'x16'

CL.

CL.

CL.

S.

REF.

25'-10"

BD RM
13'x11'

CL.

CL.

BD RM
10'x10'

CL.

UP

DWN

LIVING RM
12'x20'

31'-4"

45'-0"

UPPER LEVELS

The Pitney

Because split-levels are very popular, almost everyone is considering one type or another. If you have thought about a split-level, but think your lot is too small, here is one solution.

This compact yet roomy home is less than 30' wide, allowing it to be built on a lot as narrow as 40', depending upon local requirements.

The kitchen, with its corner-window dining area, snack bar, and utility closet, will be a focal point for family living. From the large-windowed living room, the two bedrooms and bath are only a few steps away. A stair leads up to yet another level over the kitchen.

On the basement level, a den, recreation room, utility room, and garage complete this livable plan.

AREA: First & second levels: 1,985 sq. ft.
Lower level: 494 sq. ft.

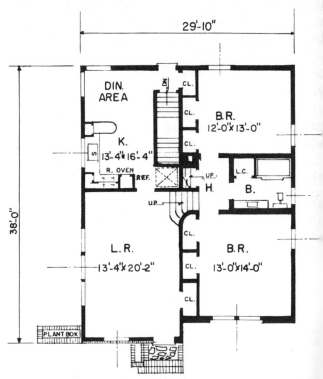

FIRST AND SECOND LEVELS

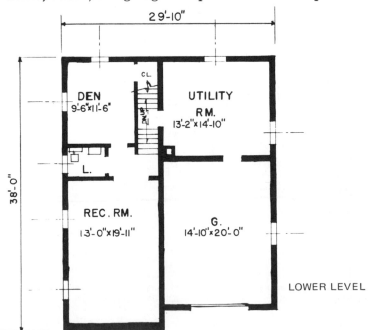

LOWER LEVEL

The Normandy

The beauty of a split-level home is threefold: it allows you to fit the house on a sloping lot, saves a great deal of stair climbing, and adds to the privacy of living. This house is so designed that it may also be constructed on level ground.

The step-saving kitchen and adjacent dinette area open into the living room with its inviting fireplace and porch entrance.

There are three bedrooms, highlighted by the master bedroom which features its own private shower-bath and two separate closets. Speaking of closets, count them: a total of 8, including a broom closet in the kitchen area.

AREA: First & Second levels: 1,240 sq. ft.
Lower level: 360 sq. ft.

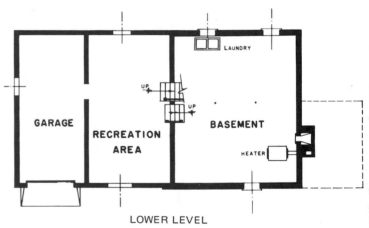

LOWER LEVEL

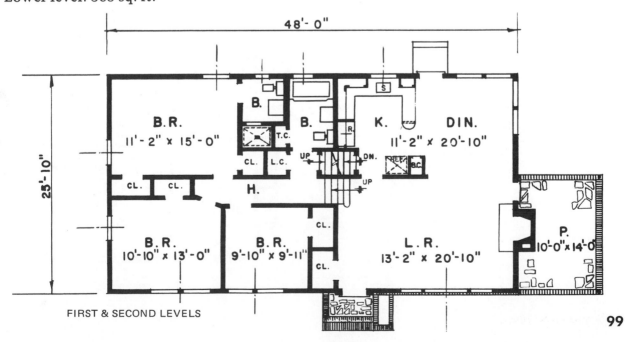

FIRST & SECOND LEVELS

The Gregory

Created to keep up with the modern trend in house building, this beautiful split-level has been designed to bring you years of happy, contented living.

For those relaxing hours, the living room, with its cheery hearth and full window, is ideal. Meal preparation and serving will be easy in the handy kitchen and sunlit dining room.

Three bedrooms, many closets, and two full baths are included in the dreamy bedroom level.

AREA: First & Second levels: 1,400 sq. ft.
Third level: 300 sq. ft.

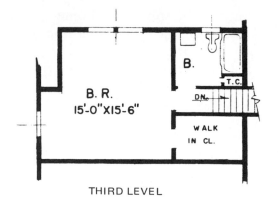

THIRD LEVEL

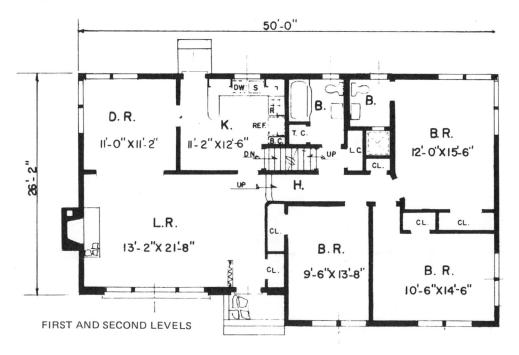

FIRST AND SECOND LEVELS

The Oakley

Here is a full-size, three-bedroom, two and one-half bath split-level complete with recreation room, garage, and full basement—and all this can be built in most areas on a 50' lot.

A most pleasing exterior is obtained in this design in spite of the narrow dimension. A covered entrance platform leads to a true center hall foyer flanked on either side by living room and dining room.

A few steps up, the family can find privacy and comfort in the three bedrooms and two baths.

AREA: First & second levels: 1,377 sq. ft.
Lower level: 345 sq. ft.

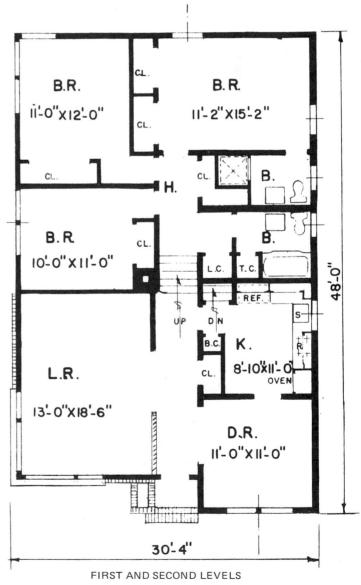

FIRST AND SECOND LEVELS

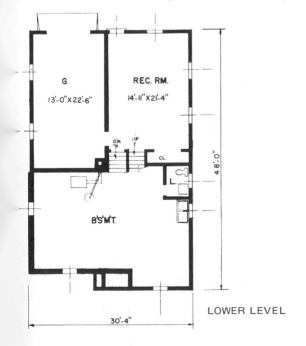

LOWER LEVEL

The Wiley

Three large, airy bedrooms line up to overlook the living area from the picturesque balcony above.

In addition to the modern, fully-equipped kitchen and spacious dining room, this living area boasts a beautiful cathedral ceiling over the living room.

Two full baths, a two-car garage, and ample closet space round out this smart design.

AREA: First & second levels: 1,390 sq. ft.
Lower level: 365 sq. ft.

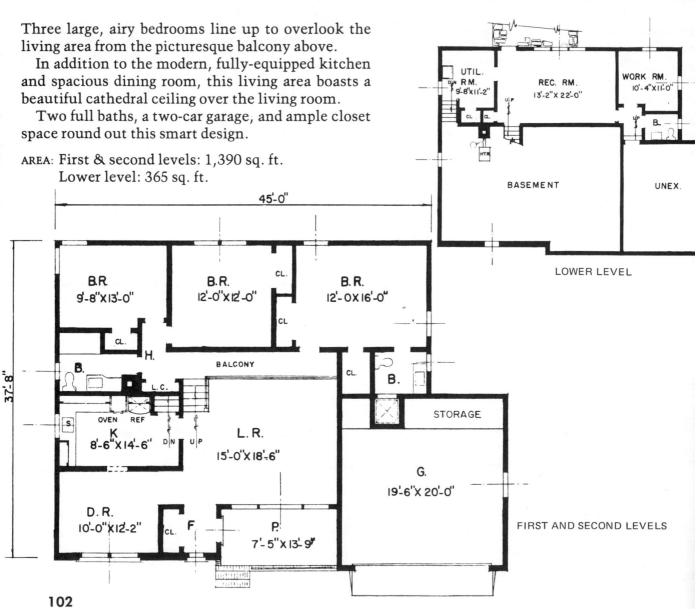

UTIL. RM.
9'-8"x11'-2"

REC. RM.
13'-2" x 22'-0"

WORK RM.
10'-4"x11'-0"

B.

BASEMENT

UNEX.

LOWER LEVEL

45'-0"

37'-8"

B.R.
9'-8"X13'-0"

B.R.
12'-0"X12'-0"

CL.

B.R.
12'-0X16'-0"

CL.

CL.

H.

BALCONY

CL.

B.

B.

L.C.

STORAGE

OVEN   REF

S

K
8'-6"X14'-6"

DN   UP

L.R.
15'-0"X18'-6"

G.
19'-6"X 20'-0"

D.R.
10'-0"X12'-2"

CL.

F

P.
7'-5"X13'-9"

FIRST AND SECOND LEVELS

The Rodney

This split-level plan offers the luxury of two floors for extra privacy with the step-saving one-floor plan.

This practical version has a huge master bedroom with private, stall-shower bathroom. The other two bedrooms share plenty of closet space and a convenient bathroom.

Down half a flight, off the front entry hall, is the 22' 6" living room with its inviting fireplace at one end and magnificent picture window. To the back is the dining room, where another picture window offers a view of the garden. The cozy den is an all-purpose room, readily adaptable as a TV room, game room, or junior living room.

AREA: First & second levels: 1,838 sq. ft.

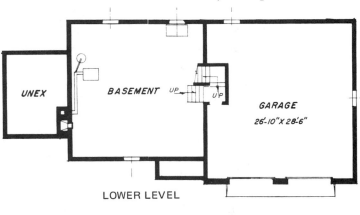

LOWER LEVEL

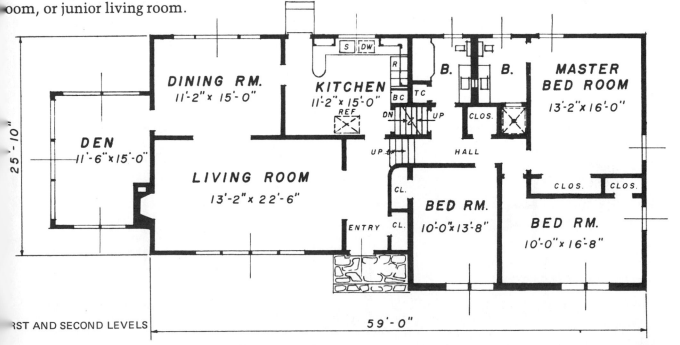

FIRST AND SECOND LEVELS

The Lowery

Every inch of space has been put to good use to bring you a beautiful, roomy split-level home for those prospective home builders with limited lots.

The sleeping level includes three spacious bedrooms and two full baths. For just plain homey living, the lower level is highlighted by the large living room, dinette, and fully-equipped kitchen.

Below, the family recreation room and two-car garage round out a design which has soared to deserved popularity.

AREA: First & second levels: 1,406 sq. ft.
Third level: 215 sq. ft.
Lower level: 220 sq. ft.

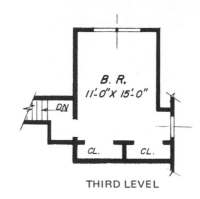

THIRD LEVEL

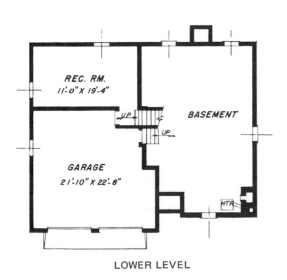

LOWER LEVEL

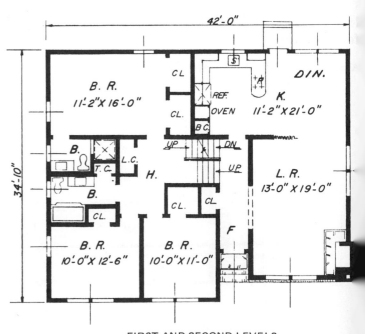

FIRST AND SECOND LEVELS

The Copley

The New England colonial farmhouse styling of this home contains behind its homey exterior a surprisingly modern arrangement of rooms. This design will give you a convenient and comfortable living experience at the most economical cost.

Basically, it is a three-bedroom, two-bath plan; because of the multi-level design, there is wonderful recreation room available with full-size windows just a few steps down from the living level. Convenient at this level also are a lavatory, laundry area, and a full two-car garage.

At the next level, above the bedrooms and over living area, is an expanded attic area large enough for as many as three additional rooms and a bath.

AREA: First & second levels: 1,487 sq. ft.
Lower level: 420 sq. ft.

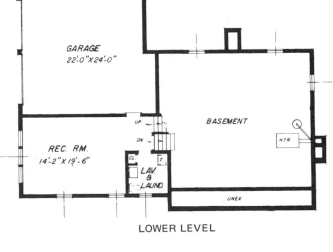

LOWER LEVEL

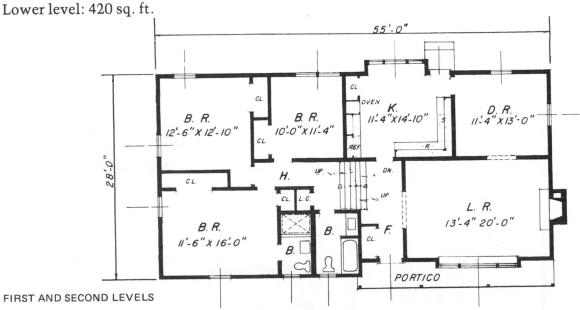

FIRST AND SECOND LEVELS

The Monterey

An abundance of closet space is featured in this attractive home. A very satisfying compromise between the two-story and the ranch style is accomplished through the split-level. Privacy is achieved for the bedrooms, yet they are only half a flight from general living areas. The convenience of a "built-in" garage should not be overlooked here.

Two authentic exteriors accompany this split-level floor plan. The choice is yours. You will not go wrong in selecting this plan. In fact, when you order the blueprints, you will receive both optional elevations, so you need not decide right now which front elevation is your favorite.

AREA: First & second levels: 1,645 sq. ft.
Lower level: 280 sq. ft.
Garage: 500 sq. ft.

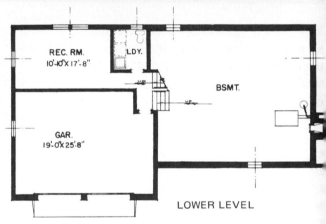

REC. RM.
10'-10" X 17'-8"

LDY.

BSMT.

GAR.
19'-0" X 25'-8"

LOWER LEVEL

The Monterey

ALTERNATE FRONT ELEVATION

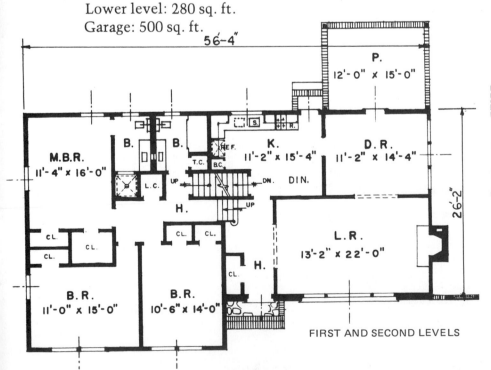

56'-4"

P.
12'-0" X 15'-0"

M.B.R.
11'-4" X 16'-0"

B.

B.

K.
11'-2" X 15'-4"

D.R.
11'-2" X 14'-4"

REF.

T.C.

B.C.

L.C.

UP

DN.

DIN.

H.

UP

S.

26'-2"

CL.

CL.

CL.

CL.

CL.

H.

L.R.
13'-2" X 22'-0"

CL.

B.R.
11'-0" X 15'-0"

B.R.
10'-6" X 14'-0"

FIRST AND SECOND LEVELS

The Woodley

Five levels, all fully usable, make this moderate-sized split-level home chock-full of living. A fully-excavated basement provides heater, laundry, and workshop areas. The second level is occupied by an extra-deep, two-car garage, a recreation room, and lavatory.

Next comes the living level with a through-hall, extended kitchen-breakfast area, a full dining room, living room, and porch.

A few steps up, we then have three full bedrooms with plenty of closets and two baths. Then, to top everything off, there is room on the top level for a future room and bath by the addition of a dormer front and rear.

AREA: First & second levels: 1,638 sq. ft.
Lower level: 300 sq. ft.

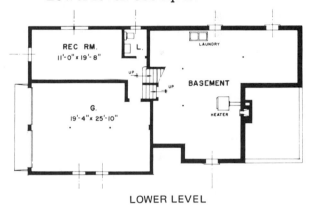

LOWER LEVEL

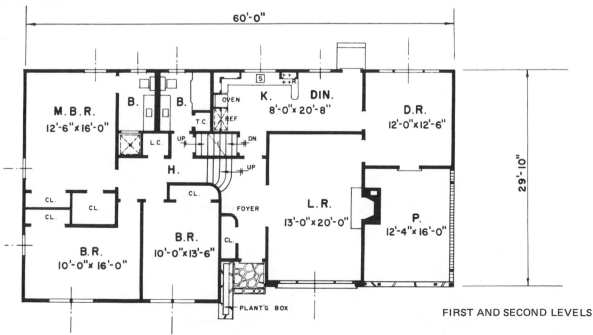

FIRST AND SECOND LEVELS

107

The Bailey

This delightful design offers convenient modern living in an attractive exterior.

The living and dining rooms combine to form a large, open area for entertaining. Just a few steps up are three bedrooms and a bath which will meet the needs of the growing family.

On the lower level, a recreation room, den, lavatory, laundry, and two-car garage complete this extremely livable plan.

AREA: First & Second levels: 1,290 sq. ft.
Lower level: 650 sq. ft.

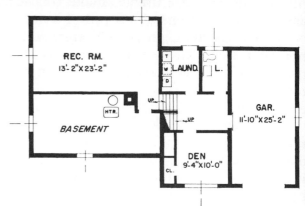

REC. RM. 13'-2" X 23'-2"

LAUND.

L.

BASEMENT

HTR.

UP.

UP

GAR. 11'-10" X 25'-2"

DEN 9'-4" X 10'-0"

CL.

LOWER LEVEL

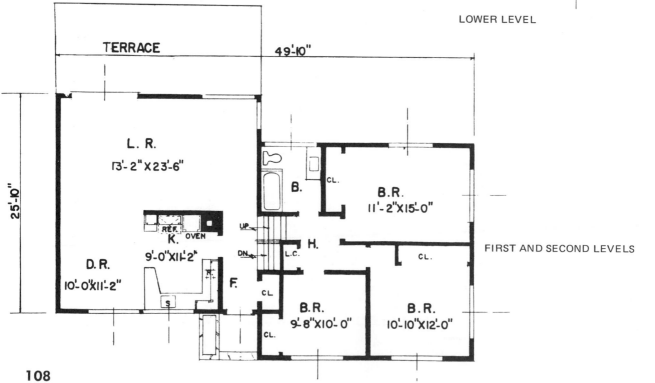

TERRACE

49'-10"

25'-10"

L. R. 13'-2" X 23'-6"

B.

CL.

B.R. 11'-2" X 15'-0"

REF. OVEN

K. 9'-0" X 11'-2"

UP

H.

L.C.

CL.

DN

D. R. 10'-0" X 11'-2"

F.

CL.

S

B.R. 9'-8" X 10'-0"

CL.

B.R. 10'-10" X 12'-0"

FIRST AND SECOND LEVELS

The Bedford

Any family will find this plan satisfying on the inside as well as attractive on the outside.

Comfort and coziness have been planned into the bedroom area, which is five steps up and away from the living area. Here you'll find three large bedrooms, two roomy baths, and all the closets you will ever need.

The living area consists of a family-sized living room accented by a cheery hearth and picture window. Adjoining, we have a sunny dining room boasting a bright corner window and an efficient, step-saving kitchen.

These and many other extras make this the home you have always dreamed of.

AREA: First & Second levels: 1,702 sq. ft.
Lower level: 255 sq. ft.

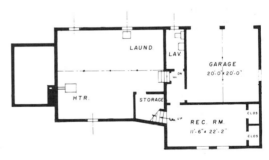

LOWER LEVEL

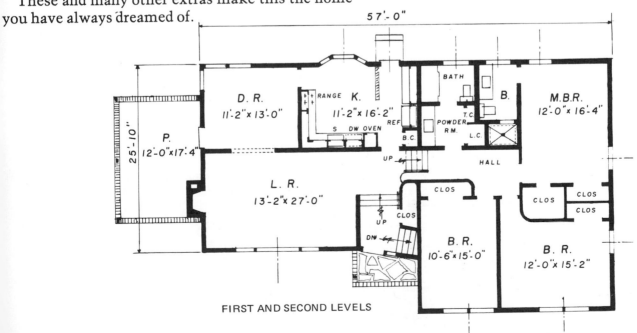

FIRST AND SECOND LEVELS

109

The Corry

This split-level home, with its barn shake and board and batten siding, combined with a box-bay window and shutters, has a truly authentic colonial appearance.

The farm kitchen, with the sink, oven, range, and refrigerator all in one unbroken L-shaped counter top, provides ample space in front of a window wall.

The bedroom level, which contains four bedrooms and two full baths, has ample closet space including a walk-in in the master bedroom.

Note the king-size recreation room with its front bay window and rear sliding glass door, which leads to the garden and patio, an ideal area for casual living. Connecting directly to this room is an over-sized, two-car garage. The doors may have an alternate front or rear location depending upon your lot conditions.

AREA: Entrance level: 564 sq. ft.
Living & Sleeping levels: 1,393 sq. ft.

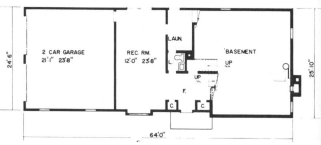

ENTRANCE LEVEL

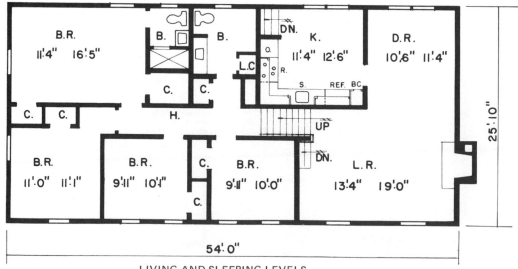

LIVING AND SLEEPING LEVELS

110

The Bentley

Graceful lines and proportions highlight this exciting split-level. Inside we find bright, cheery rooms, each well designed for the maximum of utility and comfort. The modern kitchen is typical, with its built-in, countertop range, and lots of useful cabinets.

The living level is completed by a formal dining room and spacious living room. Up just a few steps are three roomy bedrooms and two full baths.

A recreation room, garage, and basement make up the lower level of this very comfortable design.

AREA: First & Second levels: 1,650 sq. ft.
Lower level: 338 sq. ft.

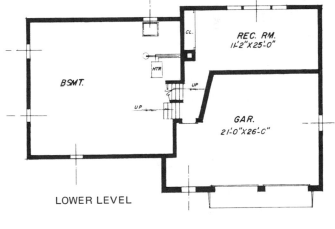

LOWER LEVEL

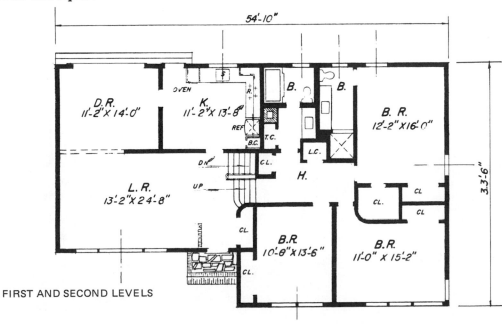

FIRST AND SECOND LEVELS

The Argosy

Here is the "different" split-level house that you've been looking for. Clean, crisp design and contrasting exterior accented by deep shadows and planting beds mark its individual character.

From the recessed split vestibule an open living room with fireplace invites you to the first level complete with dining room and large kitchen. Up four steps are four large bedrooms separated by banks of closets and two baths to assure privacy and quiet.

Downstairs the recreation room provides many hours of relaxed indoor and outdoor living through the glass doors. Note the convenience of the kitchen stair and the large basement for storage.

AREA: First & Second levels: 1,665 sq. ft.
Lower level: 335 sq. ft.

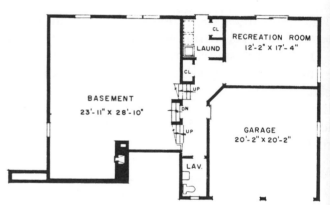

LOWER LEVEL

RECREATION ROOM
12'-2" X 17'-4"

LAUND

BASEMENT
23'-11" X 28'-10"

GARAGE
20'-2" X 20'-2"

LAV.

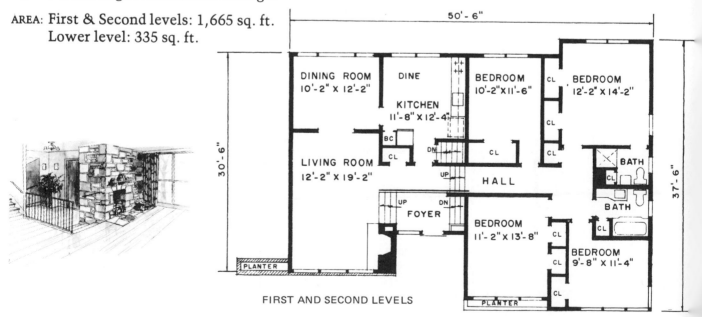

50'-6"

30'-6"

DINING ROOM
10'-2" X 12'-2"

DINE

KITCHEN
11'-8" X 12'-4"

BEDROOM
10'-2" X 11'-6"

BEDROOM
12'-2" X 14'-2"

LIVING ROOM
12'-2" X 19'-2"

HALL

BATH

BATH

UP

FOYER

BEDROOM
11'-2" X 13'-8"

BEDROOM
9'-8" X 11'-4"

37'-6"

PLANTER

PLANTER

FIRST AND SECOND LEVELS

The Rawley

This split-level beauty has been designed for those who want the finest in house planning.

The slumber level comprises three spacious bedrooms and two handy baths. A welcoming atmosphere prevails in the living level, with its extra-large living room, dining room, and roomy kitchen. The lower level contains a two-car garage and the family recreation room.

AREA: First & Second levels: 1,650 sq. ft.
Lower level: 351 sq. ft.

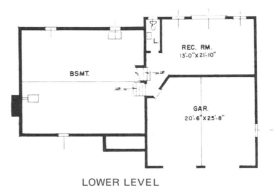

LOWER LEVEL

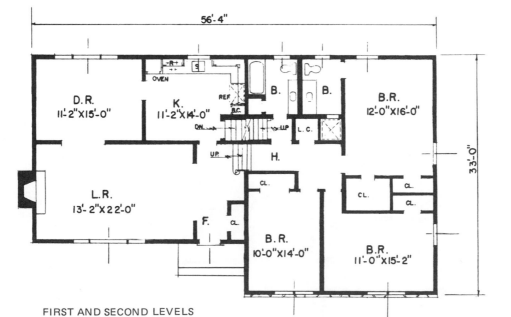

FIRST AND SECOND LEVELS

113

The Harmony

The contemporary styling of this multi-level home portrays the up-to-date living comfort which the planning provides. The on-grade entrance gives a ground-hugging character not usually found in split-level homes.

A full complement of three bedrooms and two baths makes up the sleeping level. The living level contains an extremely spacious kitchen with a projecting bay for dining.

The elaborate recreation room has front and rear exposure with sliding doors at the rear to a patio area. Nestled behind the garage and directly adjoining the rear yard is a spacious laundry-mud room.

AREA: First & Second levels: 1,498 sq. ft.
Lower level: 510 sq. ft.

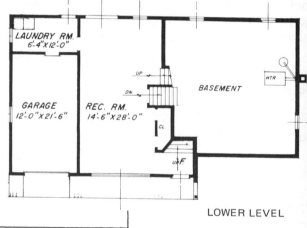

LOWER LEVEL

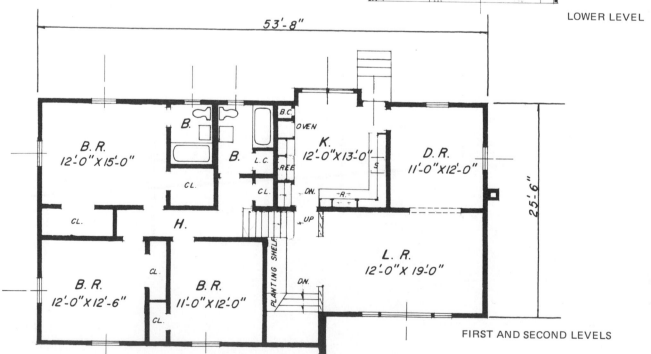

FIRST AND SECOND LEVELS

The Roxy

This striking contemporary design is as modern as tomorrow. The exterior combines those extra touches which make a home outstanding in any neighborhood. Inside, we find a wealth of features which add beauty and pleasure to family living.

Tapered slats, a cheery raised hearth, and the corner window bring a charming atmosphere to the living room. The bedroom area, a few steps above and beyond the living room, consists of three bedrooms, many closets, and two full baths.

AREA: First & Second levels: 1,670 sq. ft.
      Lower level: 350 sq. ft.

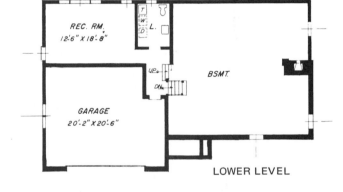

LOWER LEVEL

REC. RM.
12'-6" X 18'-8"

BSMT.

GARAGE
20'-2" X 20'-6"

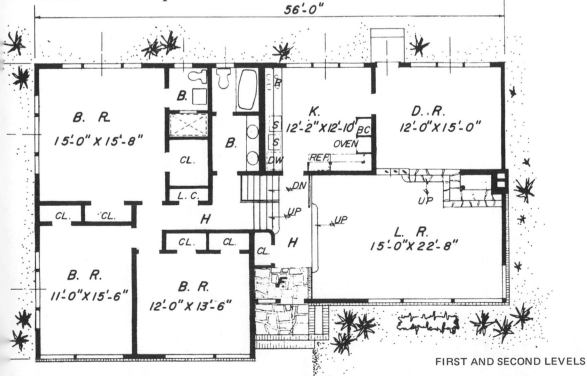

B. R.
15'-0" X 15'-8"

B. R.
11'-0" X 15'-6"

B. R.
12'-0" X 13'-6"

K.
12'-2" X 12'-10"

D. R.
12'-0" X 15'-0"

L. R.
15'-0" X 22'-8"

56'-0"

FIRST AND SECOND LEVELS

The Waverly

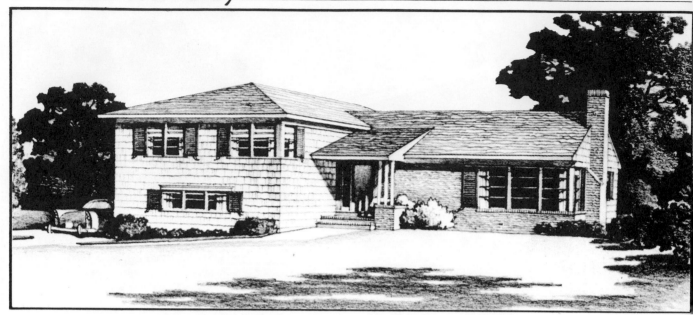

This is a perfect example of modern split-level living. Here we have all the advantages of the two-story and ranch all rolled into one breathtaking design.

The spacious, well-ventilated bedrooms, each containing extra closet space and convenient to the two full baths, have the privacy usually found only in a two-story home. Yet, it's only a few steps down to the homey living area, with its exciting living room, ample dining room, and charming kitchen.

AREA: First & Second levels: 1,690 sq. ft.
    Lower level: 350 sq. ft.

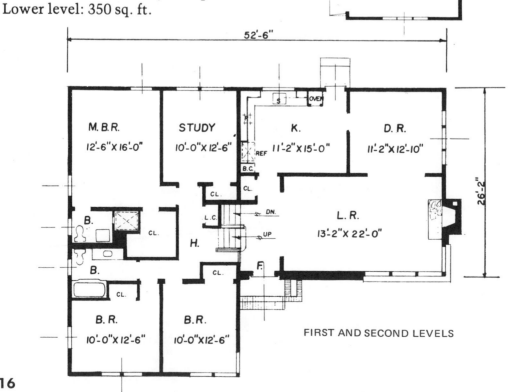

The Surrey

The charming lines of brickwork extending across and beyond the front to form a lamp-post wall give this split-level the down-to-earth feeling of growing out of the ground. The long bow-bay window enhances the front as well as broadening the effective size of the living room.

The kitchen is a dream of efficiency, with lots of work counter and a separate eating area at a large window. Two steps form the split, which practically brings this home down to the ranch level, yet still provides that slight difference between sleeping and living areas.

The garage entrance could be on the side if necessary; the plans show an alternate for this arrangement.

AREA: First & Second levels: 1,800 sq. ft.
Lower level: 255 sq. ft.

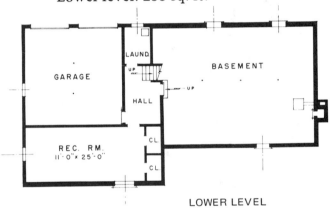

LOWER LEVEL

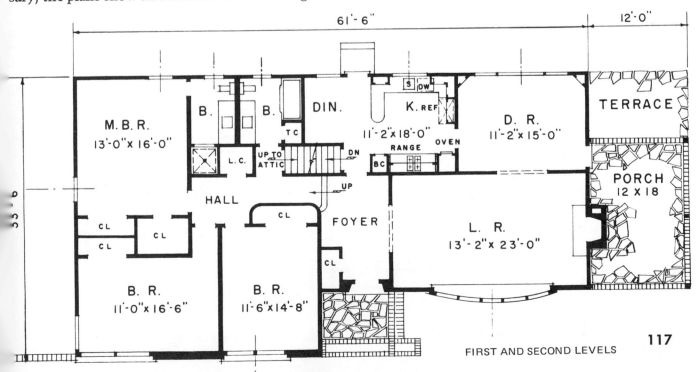

FIRST AND SECOND LEVELS

117

The Ramsay

Here is a split-level home especially designed for those who like the best in contemporary living. The bedroom area comprises three bedrooms, many spacious closets, and two full bathrooms.

The extra-large living room has a full picture window in addition to a cozy fireplace which lends a friendly atmosphere to the room. There are no steps wasted in the sunny kitchen and dining room, which have been designed to bring the maximum of efficiency.

A two-car garage and relaxing porch round out this design for better living.

AREA: First & Second levels: 1,726 sq. ft.
Lower level: 330 sq. ft.

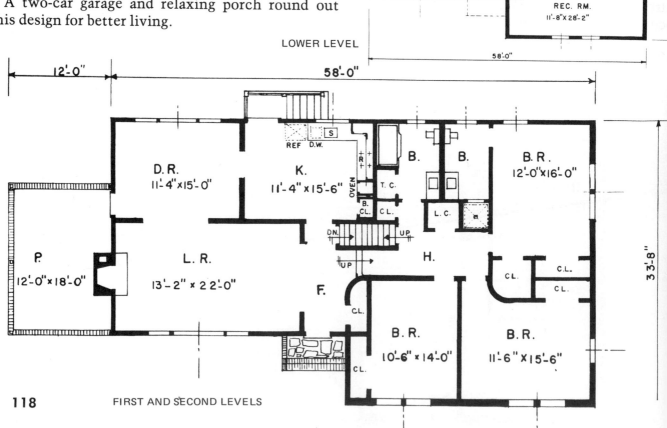

LOWER LEVEL

FIRST AND SECOND LEVELS

The Kelsey

A popular model with a slightly different twist, this split-level offers comfortable living with many luxury features in an economical plan.

Only two steps from living to bedroom areas create the separated effect and practically eliminate stair climbing.

The full-size, two-car garage still leaves room on this intermediate level for a good-sized recreation room and a lavatory. The working drawings show an alternate for locating garage doors in the side or front. There is a stair up to the attic which offers convenient access to storage in this large area.

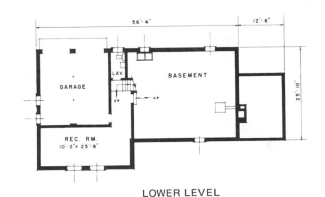

LOWER LEVEL

AREA: First & Second levels: 1,645 sq. ft.
Lower level: 425 sq. ft.

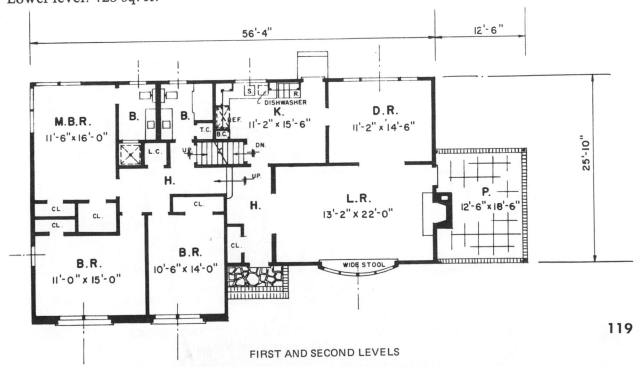

FIRST AND SECOND LEVELS

The Ardsley

Many wonderful features highlight this new, split-level rambler. This house has the feel of the all-on-one-floor ranch house, yet provides the privacy of an "upstairs."

The den, with windows on three sides, can be reached from the dining room, which, in turn, has a window wall of its own. The kitchen is directly accessible from the hall and front door and also from the garage and basement level.

The sleeping level contains three roomy bedrooms with plenty of closet space. There are two baths, back to back, with a private, glassed-in shower room for the master bedroom.

AREA: First & Second levels: 1,840 sq. ft.
Lower level: 233 sq. ft.

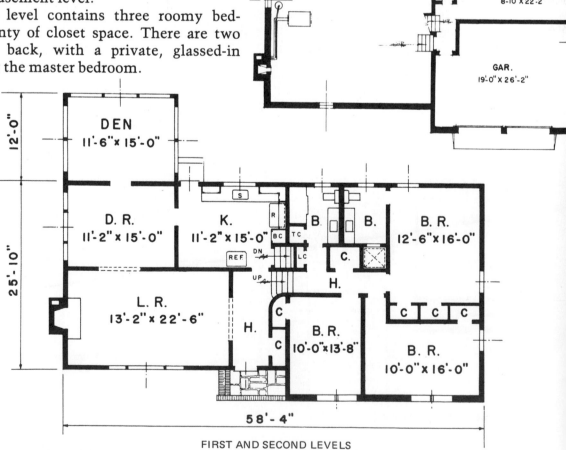

FIRST AND SECOND LEVELS

The Buckley

Contentment and comfort radiate from this split-level design. Three bedrooms to meet today's needs and a fourth, on the third level for future use, all are to be found thoughtfully included in this design.

The entrance hall leads either to an inviting living room with fireplace or to an efficient, step-saving kitchen with adjoining dining room.

The lower level contains a relaxing recreation room and a garage for the family car.

AREA: First & Second levels: 1,400 sq. ft.
       Third level: 274 sq. ft.
       Lower level: 400 sq. ft.

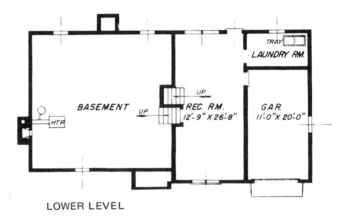

LOWER LEVEL

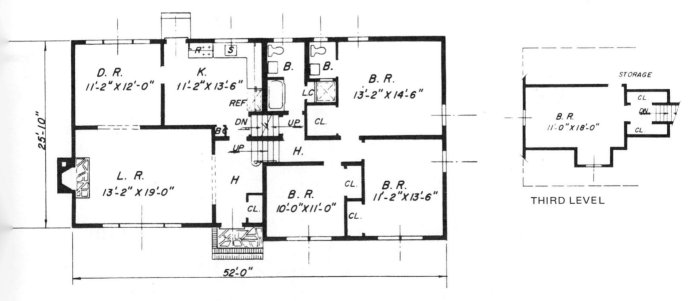

FIRST AND SECOND LEVELS

THIRD LEVEL

The Casa-Rey

"Impressive" is definitely the word to describe this appealing, Spanish-inspired, tri-level design.

On the upper level, the family will find mealtime a joy in the step-saving kitchen and formal dining room, which overlooks the living room. The sleeping area comprises three bedrooms and two baths, highlighted by the spacious master bedroom with its walk-in closet and private stall-shower bath.

The lower level provides relaxation with large family and living rooms; a study, lavatory, laundry, and garage round out this extremely livable plan.

AREA: Upper living level: 1,445 sq. ft.
Lower living level: 652 sq. ft.

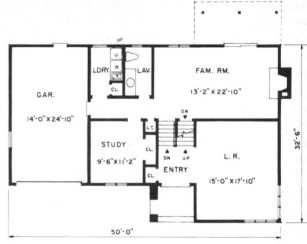

LOWER LIVING LEVEL

UPPER LIVING LEVEL

The Westley

If you dream of the charm of the Cape Cod style, yet hesitate because you like the convenience of the split-level plan, here is the home for you. All the features of split-level living are to be found in this charming Cape Cod exterior.

The plan has a tremendous kitchen, through-hall entrance, large living and dining room, three full bedrooms and two baths plus an extra bedroom and large storage room on the third level over the living area.

There are a large recreation room and lavatory plus a two-car garage under the bedroom wing. The garage enters from the rear, but the plans show an alternate for doors in the front or side.

AREA: First & Second levels: 1,700 sq. ft.
       Lower level: 400 sq. ft.

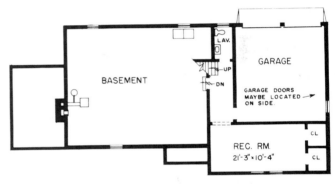

LOWER LEVEL

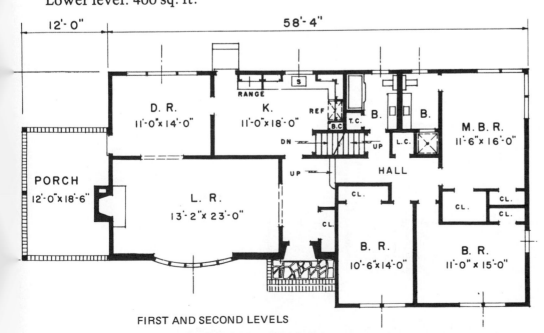

FIRST AND SECOND LEVELS

The Bradley

The most unique feature of this luxurious split-level home is the adaptation of major gas appliances for economical, carefree convenience. The basement level contains a gas dryer, furnace, hot water heater, and air-conditioning unit. A finished recreation room, lavatory, and two-car garage complete the basement-garage level.

The efficiently-designed kitchen contains a gas range, gas refrigerator, and generous counter and cabinet space. The kitchen commands easy access to the windowed dining room; a graceful arch leads to the living room with its cozy fireplace.

The sleeping quarters, comprising three bedrooms and two baths, are separated from the living area by a short flight of steps.

AREA: First & Second levels: 1,715 sq. ft.
Lower level: 450 sq. ft.

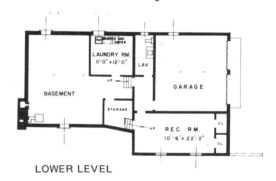

LOWER LEVEL

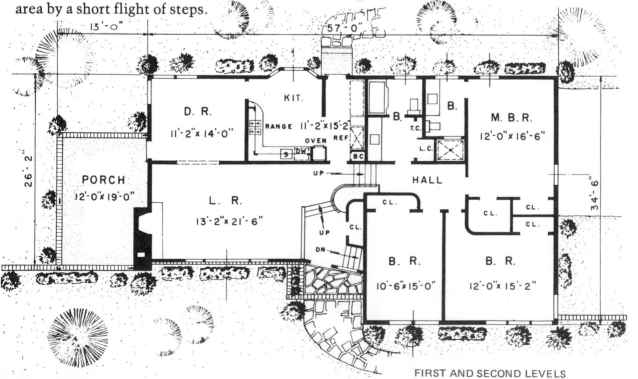

FIRST AND SECOND LEVELS

The Tracey

Many unusual, up-to-date features are incorporated in this pleasing split-level: a dramatic entrance with large glass area; beautiful foyer with steps and balcony; and a sunken living room with one wall of sliding glass.

There is convenient access from the kitchen to the porch for serving suppers and snacks, plus a separate service entrance at the rear.

Three bedrooms and two baths, plus lots of closet space, make up the sleeping level.

In addition to a full-size, two-car garage, there are a large recreation room and laundry-lavatory on the level under the bedrooms.

AREA: First & Second levels: 1,728 sq. ft.
Lower level: 445 sq. ft.

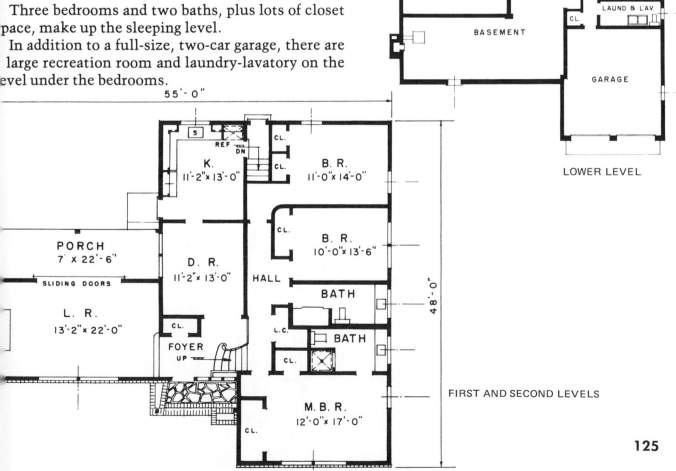

LOWER LEVEL

FIRST AND SECOND LEVELS

The Morley

Elegant living for you and your family are yours with this modern, split-level home. The living level has a cozy sunken living room, convenient kitchen-dinette area, and formal dining room with adjoining porch.

The secluded bedroom level offers privacy with three charming bedrooms, two roomy bathrooms, and all the closet space you'll ever need.

A family recreation room with connecting lavatory is found in the lower level next to a full, two-car garage.

AREA: First & Second levels: 1,830 sq. ft.
Lower level: 350 sq. ft.

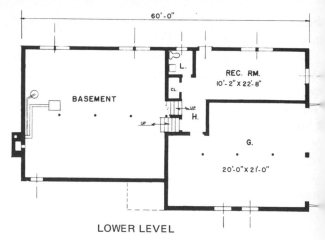

LOWER LEVEL

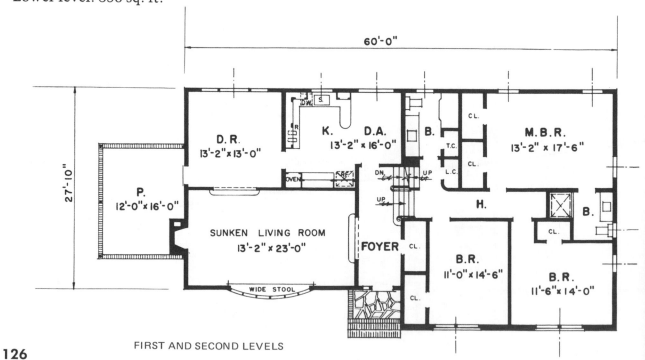

FIRST AND SECOND LEVELS

The Emery

"Something different" keynotes the planning that is to be found in this split-level design.

The lower level is formed by a two-car garage, laundry, and the comfortable family room. A few steps up, we find the kitchen and sunny living-dining room, which run across the rear of the house.

Going up a few more risers, there are three well-lighted bedrooms and two full baths.

AREA: Entrance level: 503 sq. ft.
Living level: 790 sq. ft.
Bedroom level: 752 sq. ft.

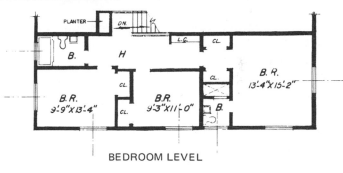

PLANTER

DN.

B.

H

L.C. CL.

B.R.
13'-4"X15'-2"

B.R.
9'-9"X13'-4"

CL.

B.R.
9'-3"X11'-0"

CL.

B.

CL.

BEDROOM LEVEL

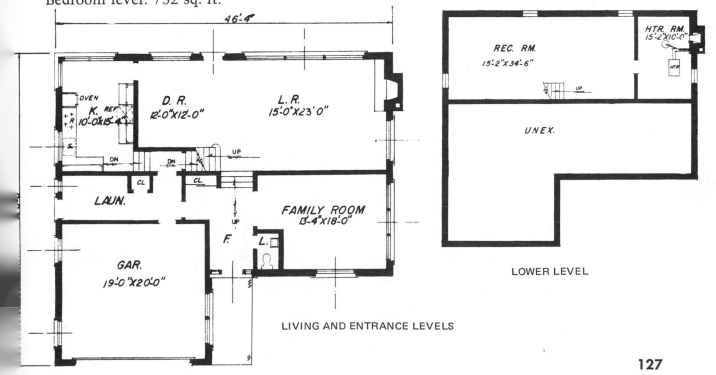

46'-4"

OVEN

K. REF
10'-0"X15'-4"

D.R.
12'-0"X12'-0"

L.R.
15'-0"X23'-0"

DN.

UP

DN.

CL.

CL.

LAUN.

UP

FAMILY ROOM
13'-4"X18'-0"

F.

L.

GAR.
19'-0"X20'-0"

LIVING AND ENTRANCE LEVELS

HTR. RM.
15'-2"X10'-0"

REC. RM.
15'-2"X34'-6"

UP

HTR

U.N.EX.

LOWER LEVEL

The Ripley

An elegant exterior complements the outstanding internal planning of this regal home.

As we pass through the foyer, which is flanked by the recreation room, we climb a few risers to the living and dining rooms with an adjoining kitchen.

The upper levels contain four bedrooms, two full baths, spacious closets, and storage room.

AREA: First & Ground levels: 1,260 sq. ft.
Second & Third levels: 940 sq. ft.

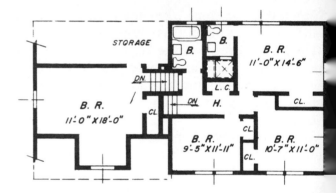

SECOND AND THIRD LEVELS

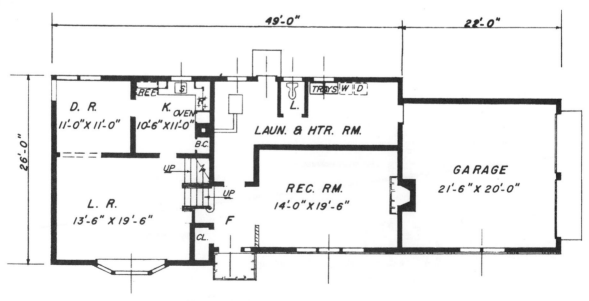

FIRST AND GROUND FLOOR LEVELS

The Ainsley

Traditional exterior details give a warm appearance to this three bedroom, split-level design, with the right side of the house featuring wood shingles, diamond-paned windows, and scalloped gable. Brick veneer is used on the front with softness supplied by a covered portico and wrought-iron arches. The excellent first impression created by the long, attractive porch is carried past the entrance door into the spacious interior.

AREA: First & Second levels: 1,900 sq. ft.
Lower level: 308 sq. ft.

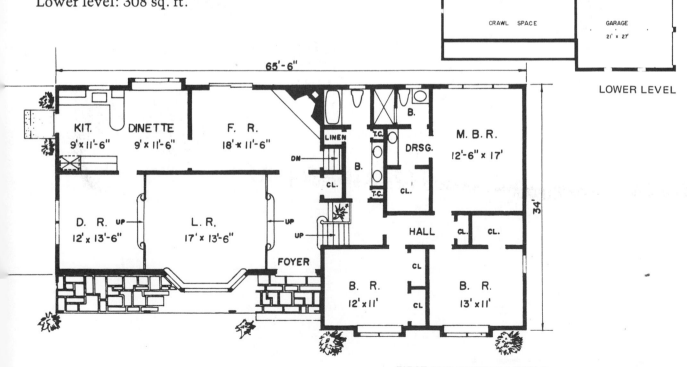

LOWER LEVEL

FIRST AND SECOND LEVELS

The Dorsey

From the circular entrance foyer, with its sweeping stairway, to the roomy, secluded family room, this split-level house represents a different, modern style of home design.

The entrance level contains a living room, dining room, and family room, all of which have access to a terrace through sliding glass doors; an efficient kitchen completes this level.

Up a few steps are three large bedrooms, two full baths, and lots of closet space.

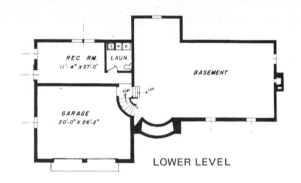

LOWER LEVEL

AREA: First & Second levels: 1,920 sq. ft.
Lower level: 308 sq. ft.

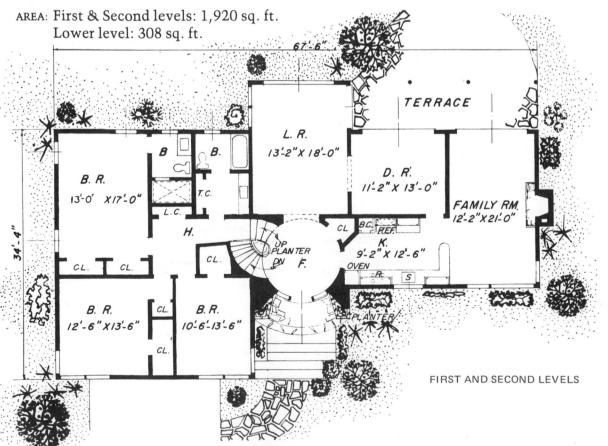

FIRST AND SECOND LEVELS

The Delray

This plan offers dignity in the exterior, with fieldstone and shingles set off by the handsome chimney and latticed overhang at the front door. Inside, a gracious hall faces a curving half-stairway to the bedroom level, where privacy and comfort are starred, and super closets and two baths (one private) are luxury extras.

On the living level, fold back the screen for an entertaining "L" or close the screen to add a TV room or study. The formal dining room and step-saving kitchen make mealtime an enjoyable experience.

On the basement level, a two-car garage, windowed recreation room, and basement complete this well-designed plan.

AREA: First & Second levels: 1,924 sq. ft.
Lower level: 305 sq. ft.

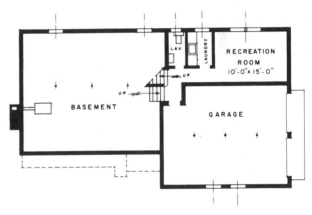

LOWER LEVEL

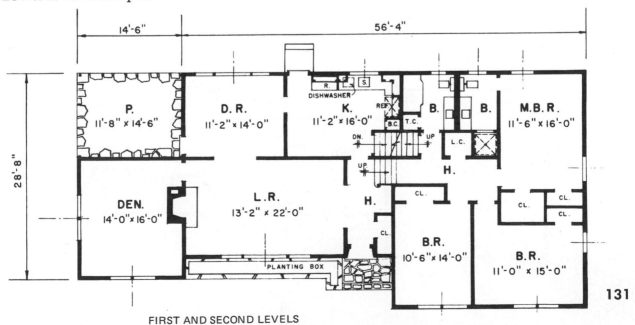

FIRST AND SECOND LEVELS

131

The Brinckley

Entrance portico, narrow clapboards, hand-split shingles, and small-paned windows are carefully blended to bring you this attractive multi-level design.

The entrance level invites you into the family room, study, laundry, lavatory, and two-car garage. Up just a few steps are the kitchen-dinette area, formal dining room, and living room with fireplace.

The bedroom level offers comfort and privacy with three bedrooms, two full baths, and lots of closets.

AREA: Living level: 1,445 sq. ft.
Bedroom level: 805 sq. ft.

26'-4"

30'-8"

CLOS

M.B.R.
12'-5" x 15'-6"

B.

CLOS

LIN.CL.

B.

DOWN

B.R.
10'-6" x 14'-0"

CLOS.

B.R.
10'-6" x 12'-2"

CLOS

BEDROOM LEVEL

72'-0"

9'-2"

24'-4"

GAR.
21'-8" x 23'-6"

F.R.
13'-4" x 19'-0"

LAUN.

CL.

B.C.

D'ETTE
9'-1" x 10'-10"

K.
10'-1" x 10'-10"

DIN.
12'-2" x 13'-4"

DN.

STUDY
11'-10" x 13'-0"

CL.

DN.

F.
9'-0" x 9'-5"

UP

DN.

L.R.
13'-0" x 19'-4"

CL.

LAV.

22'-6"

49'-6"

The Falmouth

The living area of the "ranch-split" design is all on one floor. The unusual feature of the split entrance vestibule creates an exterior appearance of the formal two-story colonial. This entrance feature also makes available the entire basement area for finished, livable rooms.

The first level comprises a living area of kitchen, dining room, and living room and a sleeping area with three bedrooms and two full baths.

On the lower level, you will find a recreation room, all-purpose room, lavatory, utility room, storage room, and garage.

AREA: First level: 1,430 sq. ft.
Lower level: 832 sq. ft.

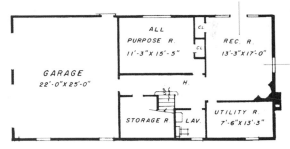

LOWER LEVEL

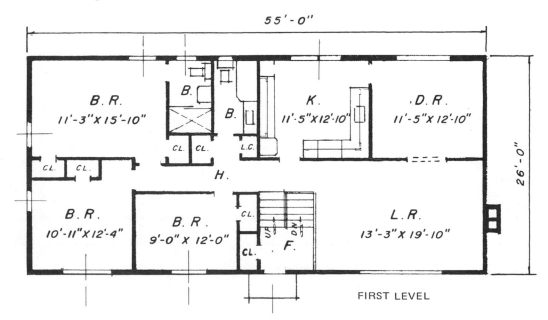

FIRST LEVEL

The Crosby

This modern split-level has the outward look of a ranch home. Two welcoming steps take us from the foyer to the large living room; from there only four more steps take us up to the family slumber area.

Located below are a maid's room, recreation area, and two-car garage. In a design like this, only a careful analysis of the actual plans will reveal all that has been included to make this home perfect for your family.

AREA: First & Second levels: 1,845 sq. ft.
Lower level: 440 sq. ft.

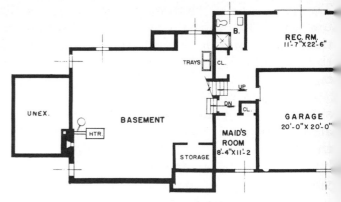

LOWER LEVEL

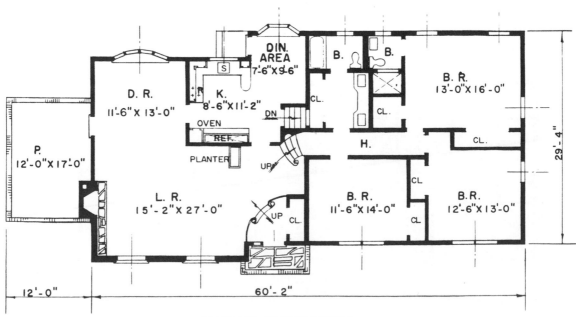

FIRST AND SECOND LEVELS

The Colony

This delightfully livable split-level home has many unusual features. The wrought-iron, columned portico across the front lends a warm colonial touch to the exterior and provides weather protection for the main entrance.

A spacious entrance foyer forms a most impressive reception area for guests. Leading up from this area is a balconied stair to the living room. Notice the kitchen, which extends to the rear and forms a bright corner-windowed breakfast area overlooking your patio.

The eight rooms and three baths in this home provide ample space for a large or growing family, plus separate areas for overnight guests and entertaining.

AREA: Living and bedroom levels: 1,492 sq. ft.
Entrance and recreation levels: 819 sq. ft.

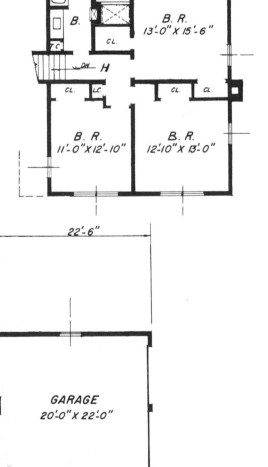

BEDROOM LEVEL

B. R. 13'-0" X 15'-6"

B. R. 11'-0" X 12'-10"

B. R. 12'-10" X 13'-0"

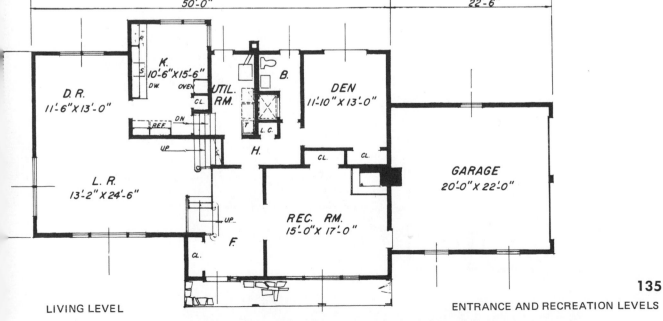

LIVING LEVEL

D. R. 11'-6" X 13'-0"

K. 10'-6" X 15'-6"

UTIL. RM.

L. R. 13'-2" X 24'-6"

DEN 11'-10" X 13'-0"

GARAGE 20'-0" X 22'-0"

REC. RM. 15'-0" X 17'-0"

ENTRANCE AND RECREATION LEVELS

135

The Westbury

Are you looking for closets? Well, here they are! Two closets in every bedroom and all full size—those in the front bedroom are extra-large, walk-in type. There's a linen closet in the hall, an extra storage closet, a towel closet in the bath, a guest closet in the entry, and a broom closet in the kitchen.

The lower level contains enormous recreation room, a lavatory, laundry, a large storage closet and garage.

Everything is large in this home—lots of kitchen with a separate breakfast alcove—a tremendous expanse of living-dining area—a beautiful porch off the side. It's all topped off by three of the most spacious bedrooms anyone could want and two full bathrooms.

AREA: First & Second levels: 1,811 sq. ft.
Lower level: 500 sq. ft.

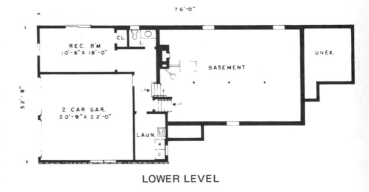

LOWER LEVEL

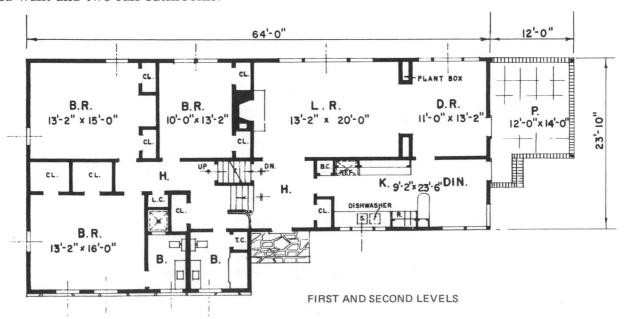

FIRST AND SECOND LEVELS

The Farley

In split-level homes, as in all other types, there are the needs of the large family to consider. Here is a plan comprising four very large bedrooms, many closets and two full bathrooms.

In addition to the regular living room, dining room, and kitchen, there is a wonderfully large porch. Just off the entrance hall, and down a few steps are situated a beautiful recreation room, laundry area, and lavatory.

Ample space throughout is provided here for the many varied activities of the large family.

AREA: First & Second levels: 1,920 sq. ft.
Lower level: 406 sq. ft.

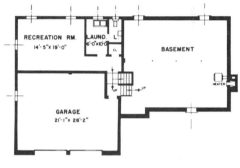

LOWER LEVEL

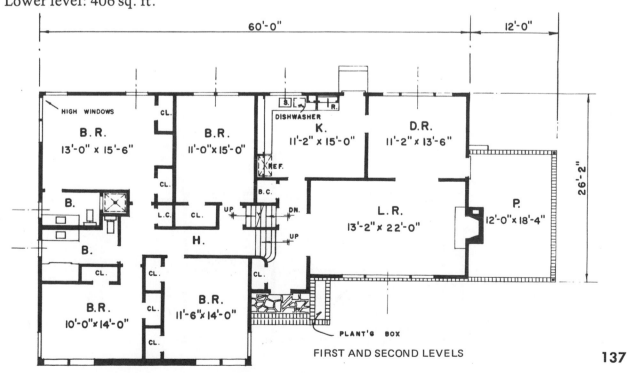

FIRST AND SECOND LEVELS

The Pomeroy

Typical of many split-level homes, this delightful house has the convenience of an all-on-one-floor design combined with the privacy that only a two-story can provide.

The bedroom level is made up of three spacious bedrooms, with large closets and two baths; one bedroom includes a dressing area.

Everyone will love the living area, which features a carefully-planned kitchen, dining room, and a friendly living room. Highlights of this design are two roomy porches and an adjoining garage.

AREA: First & Second levels: 1,520 sq. ft.
Lower level: 832 sq. ft.

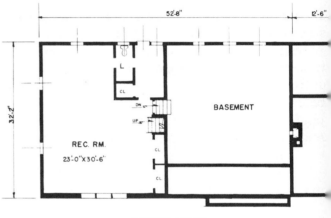

LOWER LEVEL

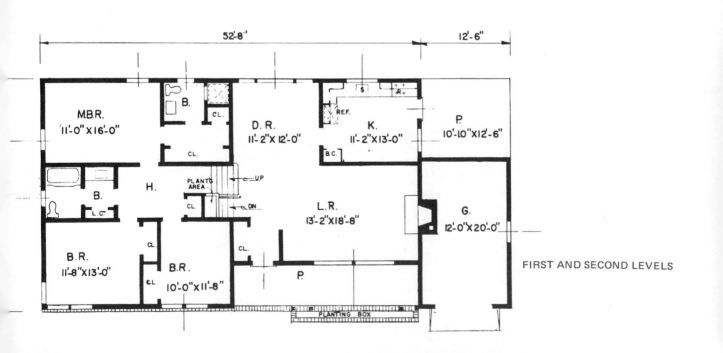

FIRST AND SECOND LEVELS

The Canterbury

This outstanding split-level home has won widespread acclaim for its new theme in home designing.

Privacy and comfortable living are starred in this four-bedroom design with its large living room and dining room and secluded family room with corner fireplace.

AREA: First & Second levels: 2,545 sq. ft.
Lower level: 400 sq. ft.

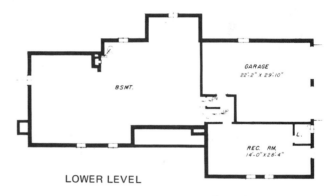

LOWER LEVEL

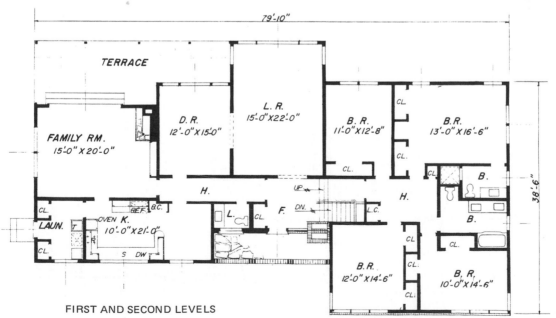

FIRST AND SECOND LEVELS

The Academy

This attractive, "ranch-look" split-level design provides comfortable living for today's family.

The living level offers space for entertaining in the large living room with fireplace, formal dining room, and efficient kitchen. The sleeping level, just a few steps up, comprises three spacious bedrooms and two full baths.

On the lower level, a recreation room, laundry, all-purpose room, and garage round out this livable plan.

AREA: First & Second levels: 1,585 sq. ft.
Lower level: 825 sq. ft.

LOWER LEVEL

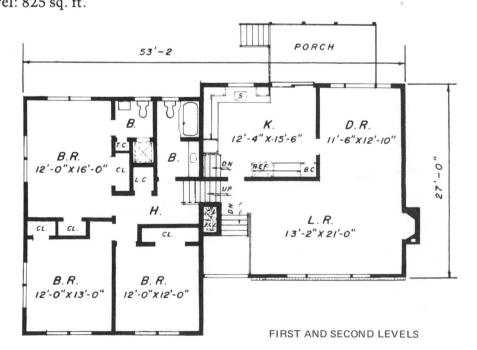

FIRST AND SECOND LEVELS

The Bellamy

The gracious exterior of this design is complemented by the comfortable living to be found inside.

The foyer, with its entry to the garage, offers the ultimate in protection for bad weather. A sunny den and connecting lavatory complete the entrance level. An open stairway leads to the living level with its large, living-dining rooms and modern kitchen.

The bedroom levels consist of four roomy bedrooms, two baths, and all the closets the family can ever use.

AREA: Ground & Living Room levels: 1,248 sq. ft.
Bedroom levels: 1,165 sq. ft.

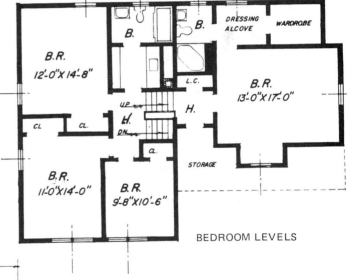

BEDROOM LEVELS

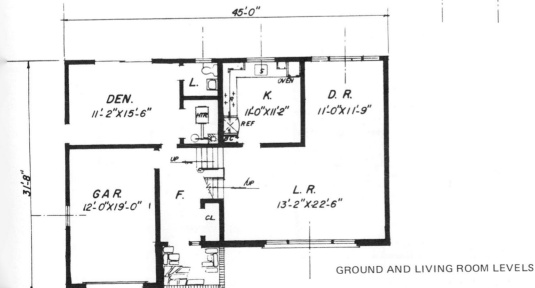

GROUND AND LIVING ROOM LEVELS

The Ashley

Comfort and luxury are apparent in a single glance at this design.

The large kitchen, a through-hall entrance, and secluded bedrooms are only a few of the advantages to be found skillfully worked into this deservedly-popular home plan.

AREA: First & Second levels: 1,740 sq. ft.
Third level: 365 sq. ft.
Lower level: 312 sq. ft.

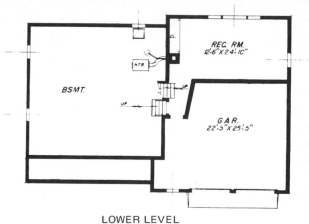

LOWER LEVEL

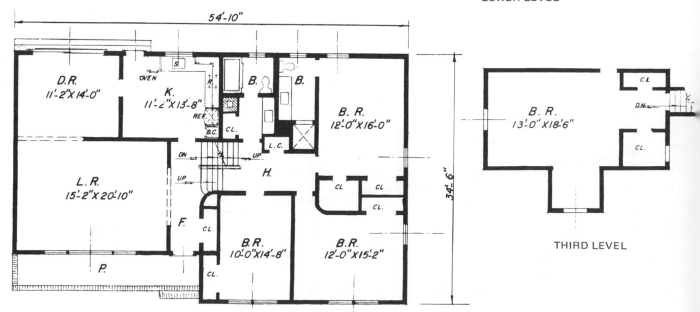

FIRST AND SECOND LEVELS

THIRD LEVEL

The Rahway

Entrance portico, narrow clapboards, brick, and small-paned windows combine to give an attractive first impression. A spacious foyer leads to a balconied living room with large picture window and colonial fireplace.

The kitchen has a picturesque curved bay window overlooking the rear garden. The lavatory adjacent to the kitchen and recreation room is located for family as well as guest use.

There are three spacious bedrooms, each having sufficient closet space. Also on this same level, you will find two lovely baths, including a stall-shower in the master bath. The oversized garage, with incorporated storage area, completes this design.

AREA: First & Second levels: 1,745 sq. ft.
Third level: 672 sq. ft.

THIRD LEVEL

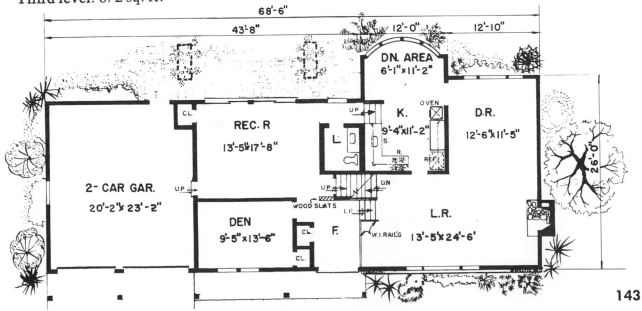

FIRST AND SECOND LEVELS

The Amity

This split-level, contemporary three-bedroom design combines the two-story and one-story construction features to offer the best of both: traditional separation of the living, sleeping, and recreation areas and the modern simplicity of a one-floor home plan.

The gentle style of this design gives it the flexibility to fit into the suburbs or city, in the mountains or desert—just about anywhere in the country, it is a home for all seasons.

AREA: Living & Sleeping levels: 2,015 sq. ft.
Lower level: 425 sq. ft.

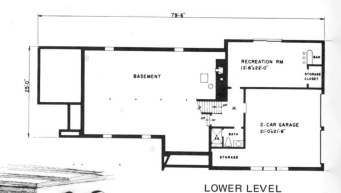

LOWER LEVEL

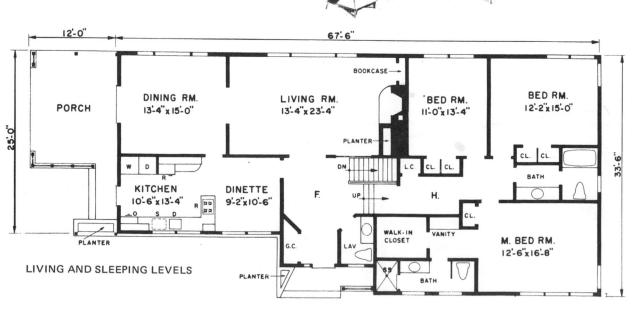

LIVING AND SLEEPING LEVELS

The Versailles

This outstanding home features a luxurious master bedroom suite with glass doors leading to a private balcony. The private bath has a free-form Roman tub. Two other bedrooms have double exposure.

The living room is directly to the left of the large foyer and adjacent to the dining room. The kitchen is enhanced by an imposing dinette area with a semi-circular floor-to-ceiling bay window.

The family room has an arched fireplace built into a brick wall. The level beneath has a two-car garage, playroom leading to backyard, and den.

AREA: First & Second levels: 1,920 sq. ft.
Lower level: 525 sq. ft.
Basement: 1,170 sq. ft.

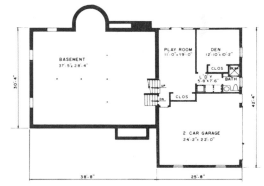

LOWER LEVEL AND BASEMENT

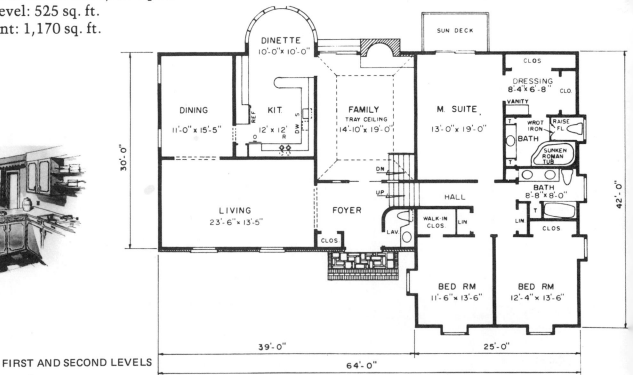

FIRST AND SECOND LEVELS

The Shrewsbury

True to its English Tudor heritage, this graceful three-bedroom split-level design offers great visual variety and makes use of traditional materials such as stucco, stone, brick veneer, rough timbers, and a textured shingle roof.

A most impressive feature of this design is the circular two-story stone-veneer tower with its heavy oak entrance door and circular entrance foyer which features a large, open, winding wrought-iron stairway leading up to the upper bedroom hall and down to the recreation room and garage.

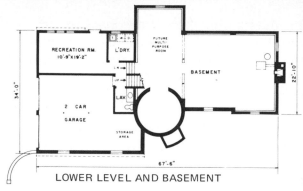

LOWER LEVEL AND BASEMENT

AREA: First & Second levels: 2,050 sq. ft.
Lower level: 400 sq. ft.
Garage: 570 sq. ft.

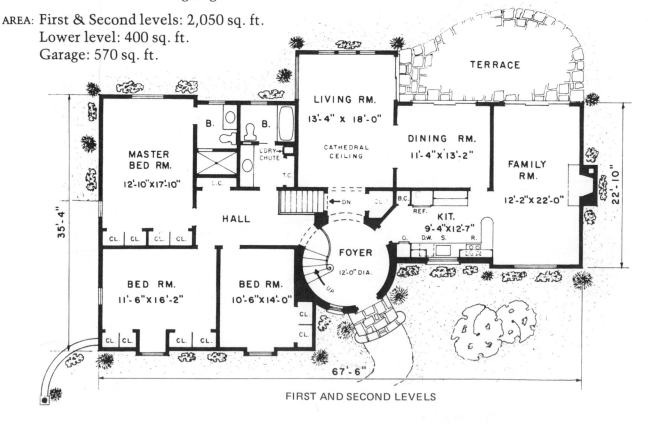

FIRST AND SECOND LEVELS

The Brookway

A split-level with an attached garage? Of course! If your family likes to spend most of its time in the recreation room, here is the plan for you. This many-purpose room has been brought up out of the basement, enlarged, and opened up to the entrance hall.

Planned for the large family, this home has an extra room on the recreation area level with a semi-private shower bath for guests or maid. There is also an open stair to the third level, which can be finished off to provide another large bedroom, bringing the total up to five bedrooms.

This home for you and your family has everything for modern living convenience.

AREA: First & Second levels: 1,715 sq. ft.
Lower level: 300 sq. ft.
Future third level: 455 sq. ft.

LOWER LEVEL AND BASEMENT

FUTURE THIRD LEVEL

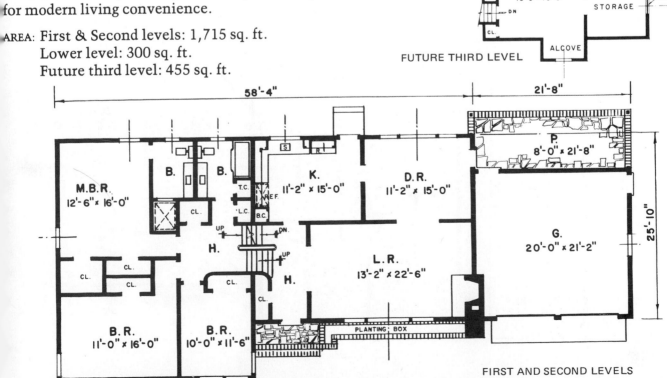

FIRST AND SECOND LEVELS

The Bradbury

This transitional design features the usual first and second levels, with a recreation room on the lower garage level and a basement a few steps below that.

The "eye-catcher" is the spacious, sunken, cathedral-ceiling living room below the adjoining dining room, and separated from it by a tapered slat divider on one side and a stone corner fireplace on the other.

The "wraparound" window unit at the front and side of the living room and the all-glass rear wall of the dining room add to the attractiveness of this area.

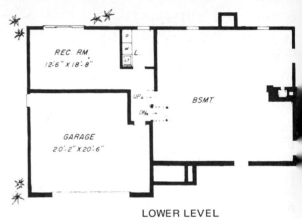

LOWER LEVEL

AREA: First & Second levels: 1,800 sq. ft.
Lower level: 395 sq. ft.
Garage: 512 sq. ft.

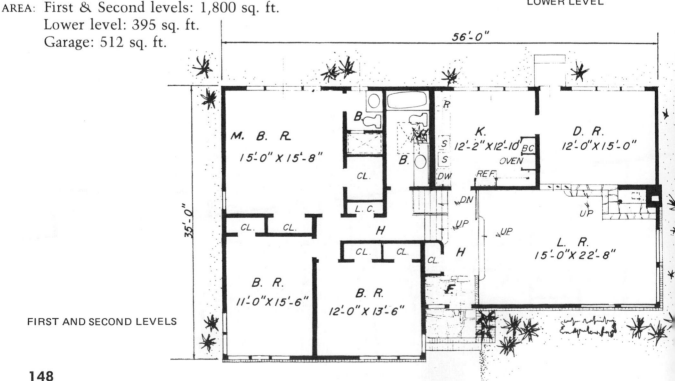

FIRST AND SECOND LEVELS

The Albany

Modern split-level living and a colonial feeling are skillfully blended to bring you a pleasing design.

Entertaining is a joy with the spacious living room, dining room, and kitchen-dinette area.

Up a few steps is a sleeping level with three bedrooms and two full baths. The large recreation room, TV room, and laundry room form a convenient work and play area.

An attached two-car garage rounds out this beautiful home.

AREA: First & Second levels: 1,740 sq. ft.
Lower level: 754 sq. ft.

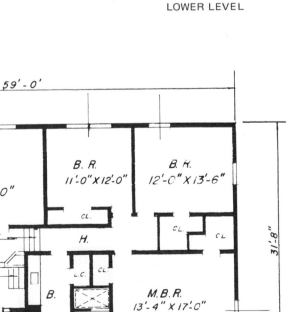

LOWER LEVEL

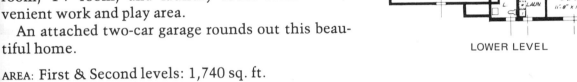

FIRST AND SECOND LEVELS

The Yardley

The exterior of this four-bedroom split-level design is contemporary in feeling with a pleasing combination of hand-split red cedar shingles, brick veneer, multi-unit single-paned windows, and low-hipped and gabled asphalt-shingled roofs.

For those who can orient themselves to "split-level" living, this carefully planned design, with a long list of features to recommend it, offers visual satisfaction on the outside and practical living on the inside.

AREA: Living levels: 1,375 sq. ft.
Bedroom level: 1,139 sq. ft.

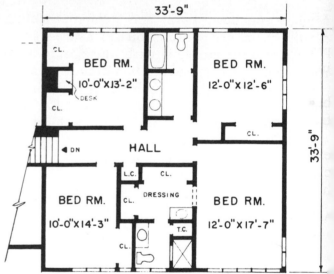

33'-9"

33'-9"

CL.
BED RM.
10'-0"X13'-2"
DESK
CL.

BED RM.
12'-0"X12'-6"

CL.

HALL

DN

L.C. CL.
DRESSING
CL.

BED RM.
10'-0"X14'-3"

T.C.

BED RM.
12'-0"X17'-7"

CL.

BEDROOM LEVEL

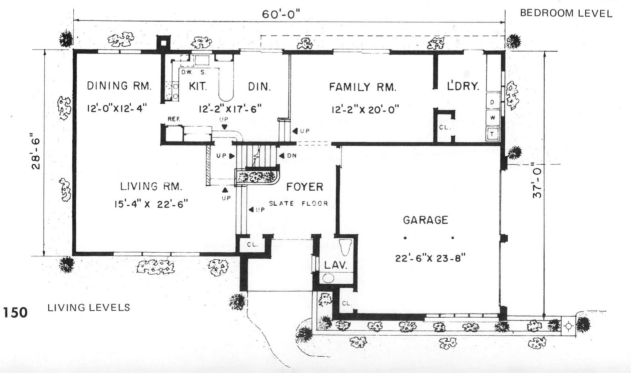

60'-0"

28'-6"

DINING RM.
12'-0"X12'-4"

DW. S.
KIT.
12'-2"X17'-6"
REF.

DIN.

FAMILY RM.
12'-2"X 20'-0"

L'DRY.
D
W
CL. T

UP

UP DN

LIVING RM.
15'-4"X 22'-6"

UP

FOYER
SLATE FLOOR

UP

37'-0"

CL.

LAV.

GARAGE
22'-6"X 23'-8"

CL.

The Hillery

This is really colonial split-level living at its finest. The best features of the traditional and the contemporary have been blended to bring you an outstanding home.

For those slumber hours, you will appreciate the bedrooms being only five short steps up and away from the living room.

Everywhere you look, you find those wonderful extras like two fireplaces, big window areas, closets, etc. which we all desire in that dream house.

AREA: First & Second levels: 1,770 sq. ft.
       Lower levels: 750 sq. ft.

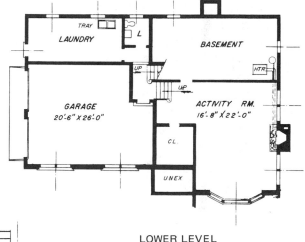

LOWER LEVEL

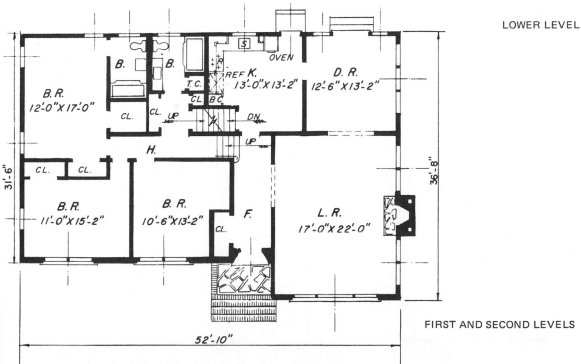

FIRST AND SECOND LEVELS

The Montgomery

Wrought-iron posts and railings, brick, and shutters are carefully blended to bring you this attractive split-level design.

The living level offers room for entertaining with a huge, open living-dining room arrangement. The adjoining kitchen-dinette area completes this level.

There are ample sleeping accommodations, with three spacious bedrooms, each having sufficient closet space. Provision has also been made for a fourth bedroom if needed.

The entrance level provides a two-car garage, laundry, and powder room, and multi-purpose room.

AREA: First & Second levels: 1,820 sq. ft.
Third level: 225 sq. ft.
Entrance level: 490 sq. ft.

SECOND AND THIRD LEVELS

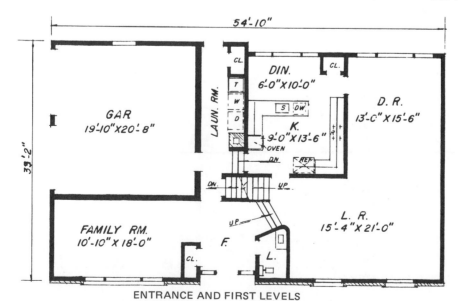

ENTRANCE AND FIRST LEVELS

The Finley

The pleasing exterior of this attractive split-level is complemented by the interior planning for the family's convenience.

Three large bedrooms and two baths overlook the living area, which is just a few short steps below.

Here we behold modern comfort skillfully planned into the inviting living room, sunny dining room, and convenient kitchen.

Ample provision has been made in the basement level for work and recreation rooms.

AREA: First & Second levels: 1,670 sq. ft.
Third level (future): 237 sq. ft.
Lower level: 660 sq. ft.

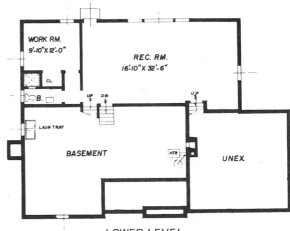

LOWER LEVEL

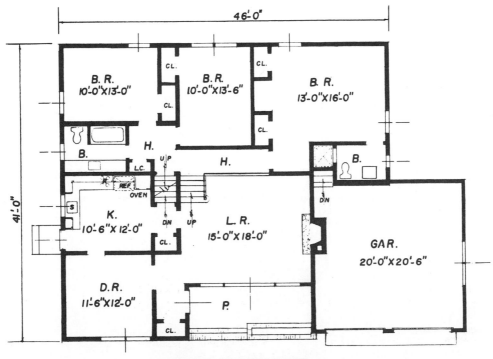

FIRST AND SECOND LEVELS

The Berkley

The dramatic exterior appearance of this home carries throughout the interior. A large entrance foyer leads up to the bedroom wing and another short flight to the extra third level bedroom. Down half a flight from the foyer are a recreation room, lavatory, laundry, and two-car garage.

The living and dining rooms, separated unobtrusively by planters, give an unbroken expanse of 35'. The kitchen, almost 24' long, includes all the latest features plus a bright corner-window breakfast alcove.

The bedroom level comprises three roomy bedrooms, two full baths, and lots of closet space.

AREA: First & Second levels: 1,800 sq. ft.
Lower level: 310 sq. ft.
Third level: 500 sq. ft.

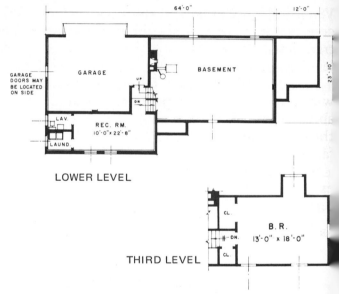

LOWER LEVEL

THIRD LEVEL

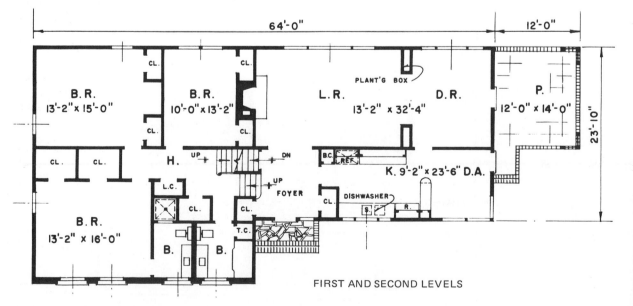

FIRST AND SECOND LEVELS

The Ormsby

Visions of royal living and spaciousness nestling in a countryside come quickly to mind in looking at this traditional French Provincial three-bedroom, split-level design.

The angular, diamond-glazed living room bay window, wrought-iron balconied dormer windows, shutters, and brick exterior with brick quoins on the end of the building help convey a feeling of old-fashioned quality.

Radiating an image of living elegance, this design exhibits artistic lines on the exterior and a lavish interior layout.

AREA: First & Second levels: 2,282 sq. ft.
Lower level: 370 sq. ft.

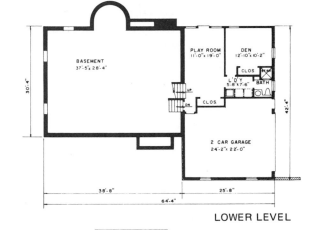

LOWER LEVEL

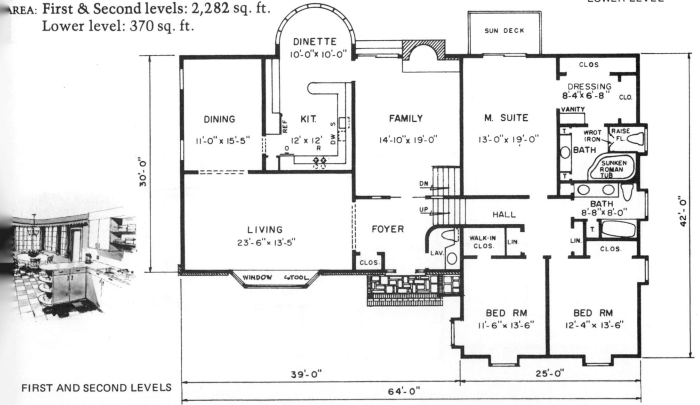

FIRST AND SECOND LEVELS

The Barnsley

Split-levels have matured into a distinct style of their own, exemplified by this appealing design, which can be outstanding in any setting.

Five steps up from the entrance foyer is the secluded upper level, with its three bedrooms and two full baths. There are two closets in every room and an extra large walk-in for the master bedroom.

On the living level, the family will find plenty of room for relaxation in the living room, cozy den, formal dining room. This level is completed by the efficient kitchen and adjacent dining area.

The lower level offers a recreation room, laundry, lavatory, two-car garage, and basement.

AREA: First & Second levels: 2,151 sq. ft.
       Lower level: 585 sq. ft.
       Basement: 1,065 sq. ft.

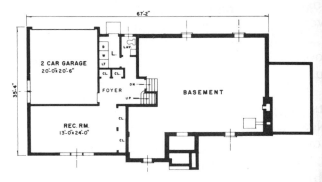

LOWER LEVEL

FIRST AND SECOND LEVELS

The Crowley

Presenting a regal exterior of brick veneer, clapboards, and picturesque shutters, this design has won widespread acclaim.

The lower level contains a two-car garage, a play room, and, if desired, a maid's room complete with full bath.

Above, we find the welcoming living room with its sunny bow window, fireplace, and planters. Nearby are a lavatory, laundry room, and a large den containing sliding glass doors on two sides.

Luxury best describes the slumber level, with its three large bedrooms, two complete baths, and the numerous closets that abound here.

AREA: First & Second levels: 2,340 sq. ft.
Lower level: 405 sq. ft.

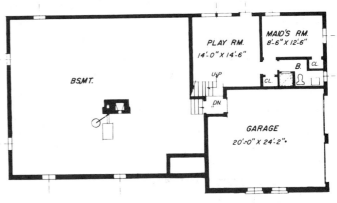

LOWER LEVEL

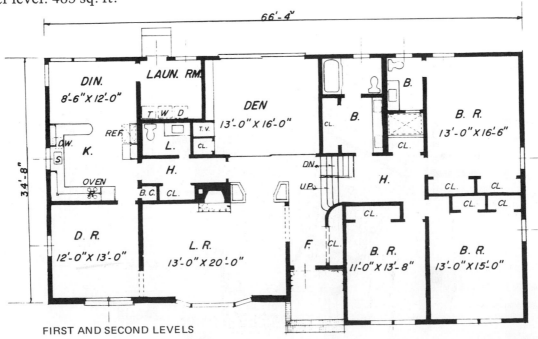

FIRST AND SECOND LEVELS

157

The Murray

From its two-car garage at one end to the bedroom levels at the other, this split-level offers something a little different in home design.

The handsome foyer has two large closets and a handy powder room. A long planting box separating the large dining room and super-sized activity rooms adds a refreshing touch.

The bedroom levels comprise three roomy bedrooms, an inviting den, and two full baths.

AREA: First & Second levels: 2,100 sq. ft.
Lower level: 663 sq. ft.

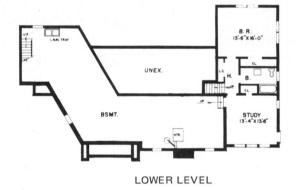

LOWER LEVEL

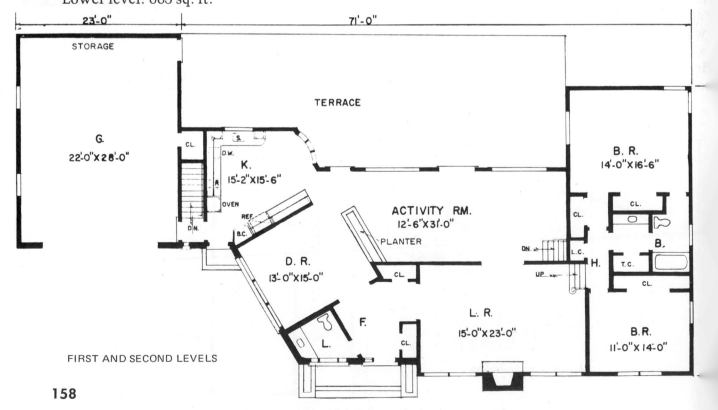

FIRST AND SECOND LEVELS

The Tamarind

This multi-level design is contemporary in spirit and styling. It features vertical redwood siding, random-width fieldstone, low-pitched roofs. Clerestory and canopied casement windows add architectural interest.

Off the entrance foyer is a sloped, beamed-ceiling living room and a family room with corner fireplace. The kitchen is a delight highlighted by a dramatic circular all-glass dinette area.

The luxurious master suite on the upper level has its own dressing area, two huge closets, and a private bath with sunken Roman bathtub. The other two bedrooms share a convenient bath.

The lower level comprises two-car garage, recreation room, den or hobby room, shower bathroom, complete laundry, and full basement.

AREA: First & Second levels: 2,290 sq. ft.
Lower level: 550 sq. ft.

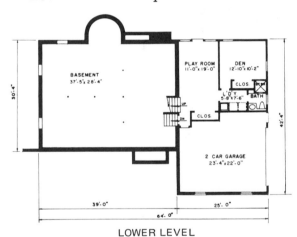

LOWER LEVEL

FIRST AND SECOND LEVELS

The Thackeray

This ten room home can meet all the demands of the large family. The large living room with wall fireplace connects directly to an oversized dining room thus offering an ideal entertainment area. The family room, also with fireplace, opens directly to a raised terrace.

Note the spacious, farm-type kitchen, located off the foyer and connecting directly to the dining room and laundry room.

Up just five steps is the bedroom level, consisting of three bedrooms, a den or fourth bedroom, lots of closets, and two full baths.

A two-car garage, recreation room, and lavatory make up the lower level of this design for the large family.

AREA: First & Second levels: 2,500 sq. ft.
Lower level: 378 sq. ft.

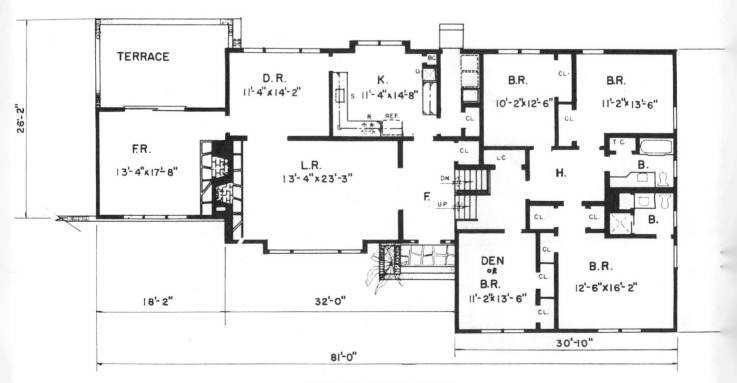

FIRST AND SECOND LEVELS

The McKinley

This handsome split-level design is an outstanding home for the large, active family. On the entrance level, we find a huge recreation room, cozy den with fireplace, and convenient lavatory.

The living level contains a large living room, opening to a formal dining room which adjoins the step-saving kitchen.

Three bedrooms and two full baths make up the bedroom level. Up just a short flight of steps, there is space for two additional bedrooms and a bath.

AREA: Entrance level: 720 sq. ft.
   Living & Bedroom levels: 1,576 sq. ft.
   Fourth level bedrooms: 700 sq. ft.

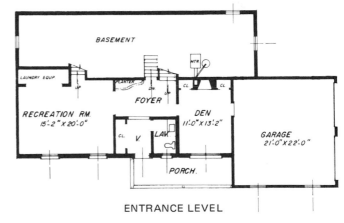

ENTRANCE LEVEL

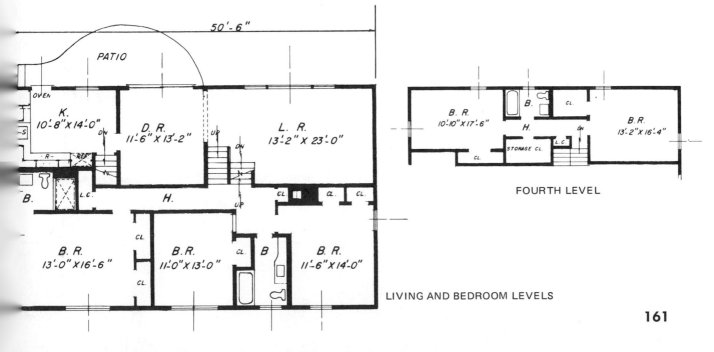

LIVING AND BEDROOM LEVELS

FOURTH LEVEL

The Chandler

Dramatic interest and good planning prevail throughout this three bedroom, contemporary split-level design. The weather-protected, double-door entrance is highlighted by the "floor-to-ridge" glass treatment, which floods the cathedral-ceiling foyer with daylight.

The dinette, kitchen, and family room feature a stone-faced fireplace in a combination of 37 feet of open space. Two compartmented bathrooms provide the ultimate in service for the three large bedrooms.

Wide steps lead down to the sunken living room from the foyer and dining room, and directly under the bedrooms are the two-car garage, recreation room, lavatory, and laundry with convenient access to the upstairs foyer.

AREA: First & Second levels: 2,533 sq. ft.
Lower living area: 552 sq. ft.

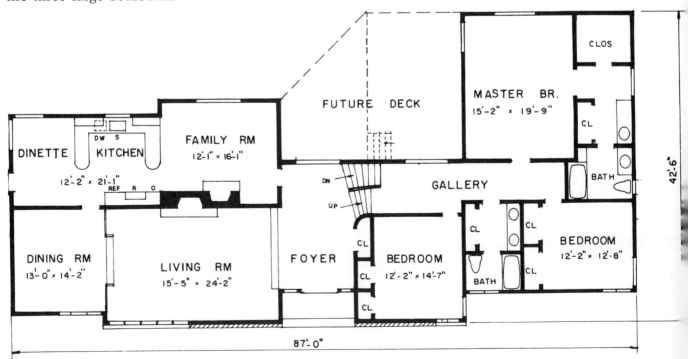

FIRST AND SECOND LEVELS

The Tierney

Featuring the long, low silhouette we usually attribute to a ranch home, this roomy split-level has been designed to offer the maximum in gracious living.

From the utility and family rooms at one end to the sleeping area with its four large bedrooms and two complete baths at the other, little is left to be desired.

Below the bedroom level we find a generous recreation room and a two-car garage.

AREA: First & Second levels: 2,630 sq. ft.
Lower level: 470 sq. ft.

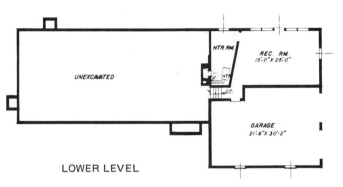

LOWER LEVEL

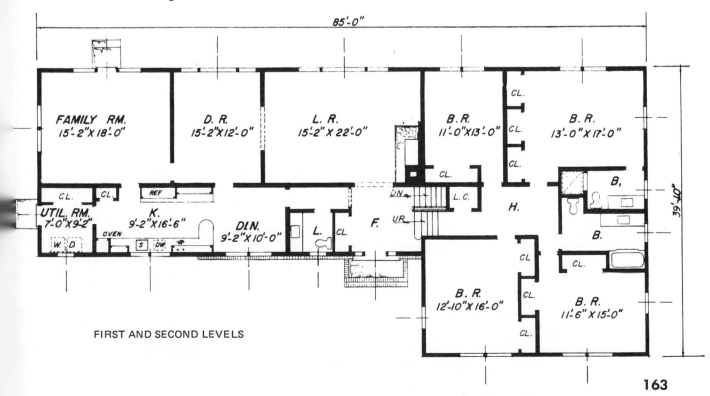

FIRST AND SECOND LEVELS

The Fairway

The aristocratic colonial charm presented by this lovely home lends warmth and splendor to the contemporary arrangement of rooms within. Spaciousness is the theme, as is readily apparent from a glance at the room sizes indicated.

Convenience is inherent with all major areas accessible from the main foyer. The family room is directly adjacent to the kitchen and outdoors for patio and barbecue areas.

AREA: First & Second levels: 2,730 sq. ft.
Lower level recreation room: 410 sq. ft.

LOWER LEVEL

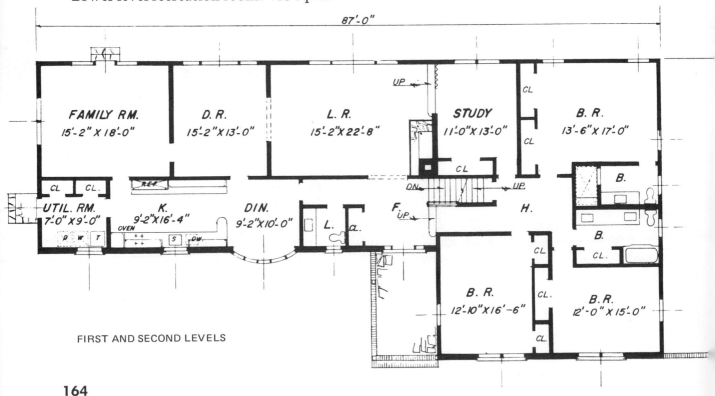

FIRST AND SECOND LEVELS

The Seville

This authentic Spanish split-level embodies easy, informal living indoors and exterior styling of rough stucco, circular headed windows, turned wood posts, and projecting, stained wood beams.

Arranged for present-day living, the plan features a daylight cathedral-ceiling entrance foyer with a split stair leading to the lower activity area.

AREA: Living & Sleeping level: 2,175 sq. ft.
Lower level: 966 sq. ft.

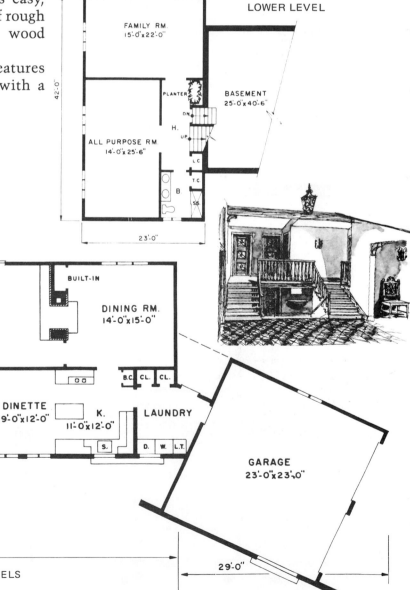

LOWER LEVEL

FAMILY RM.
15'-0"x22'-0"

PLANTER

BASEMENT
25'-0"x40'-6"

ALL PURPOSE RM.
14'-0"x25'-6"

DN.

H.

UP

L.C.

T.C.

B.

S/S

42'-0"

23'-0"

M. BATH

CL.

DRESS'G.

CL.

M. BED RM.
13'-0"x18'-0"

LIVING RM.
14'-0"x24'-0"

BUILT-IN

DINING RM.
14'-0"x15'-0"

W.I. CL.

BED RM.
11'-6"x12'-0"

CL.

CL.

L.C.

H.

UP

DN

F.

G.CL.

CL.

B.C.

CL.

CL.

DINETTE
9'-0"x12'-0"

K.
11'-0"x12'-0"

LAUNDRY

S.

D.

W.

L.T.

GARAGE
23'-0"x23'-0"

BED RM.
12'-0"x12'-0"

T.C.

CL.

CL.

T.C.

BATH

POWDER RM.

65'-0"

29'-0"

LIVING & SLEEPING LEVELS

The Roxbury

The rich, graceful lines of this home extend from the overall exterior appearance, through the entrance, into the living room and spread throughout the interior.

Off the living room at the front is the TV room, which leads to the airy porch. The efficient kitchen and dinette have doors leading both outside and to the recreation room.

The bedroom wing consists of three very large bedrooms, spacious closet area, and two full bathrooms.

The plans give an alternate arrangement showing the garage entrance on the front.

AREA: First & Second levels: 2,206 sq. ft.
Lower level: 960 sq. ft.

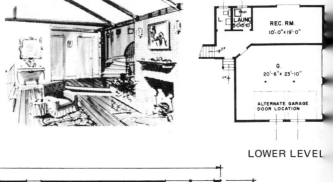

LOWER LEVEL

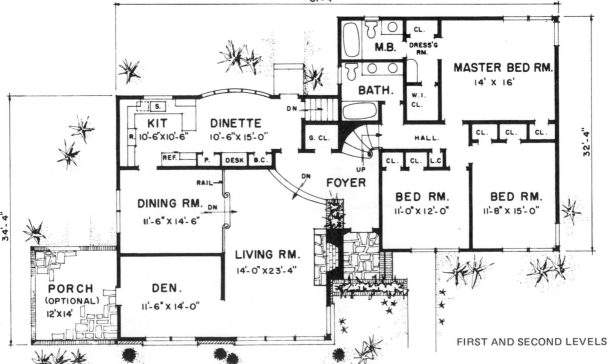

FIRST AND SECOND LEVELS

The Inverrary

This multi-level design has been inspired by the ever-popular Spanish feeling. The entrance foyer acts as a central distribution point leading into the spacious living room and up to a dining room and country kitchen-dinette.

The family room and kitchen-dinette have convenient access to the large rear sun deck. From there, you go upstairs to the three-bedroom level and continue up to yet another bedroom on an upper level.

On the lower level are the recreation room, laundry room, and a two-car garage.

AREA: Living level: 1,538 sq. ft.
Sleeping level (including fourth bedroom):
1,763 sq. ft.
Lower level: 575 sq. ft.

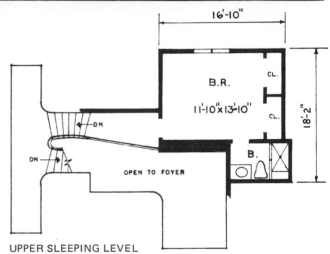

UPPER SLEEPING LEVEL

LOWER LEVEL

LIVING AND SLEEPING LEVELS

167

The Middlebury

This home is perfect for the narrow lot, because it can fit on most 50′ lots. This plan is ideal for the young, budget-minded family.

The upper level contains a spacious living-dining area, step-saving kitchen, three ample bedrooms, and a central bath.

The lower level offers even more room for relaxation in the recreation room and den. A laundry, lavatory, utility room, and garage complete this livable plan.

AREA: Upper level: 965 sq. ft.
Lower level: 671 sq. ft.

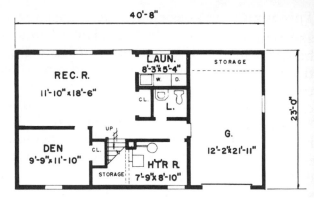

LOWER LEVEL

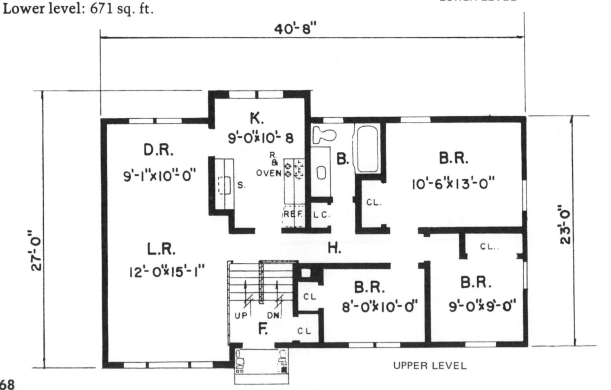

UPPER LEVEL

The Monticello

All the charm and elegance of colonial styling are apparent in this bi-level, three bedroom, ranch home with its gabled-roof entrance portico, shutter-trimmed multi-paned windows, handsome entrance, and facade of brick veneer and red cedar clapboards.

Inside, entertaining and meal preparation will be relaxed and enjoyable in the living room-dining room area and the efficient kitchen. The sleeping quarters on the same level afford comfort and privacy in three bedrooms and two baths.

On the lower level, we find a family room, den, laundry, lavatory, and garage, which complete this well-designed plan for today's family.

AREA: **Upper level**: 1,205 sq. ft.
Lower level: 541 sq. ft.
Garage: 628 sq. ft.
Deck: 83 sq. ft.

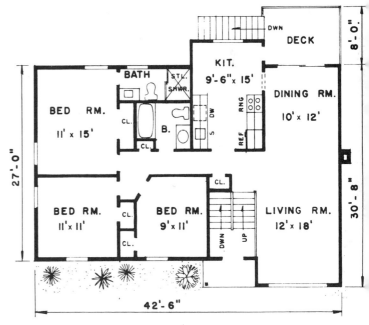

UPPER LEVEL

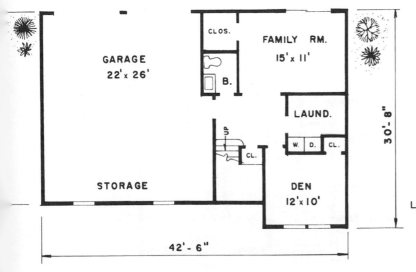

LOWER LEVEL

The Adams

Modern living is the idea of this bi-level. Clean design and a friendly entrance invite you to enjoy the roominess of three bedrooms, two baths, large step-saving kitchen, living room, and dining room.

The lower level continues the mood, opening to a creative recreation room with corner fireplace and window door access to the patio. Note the privacy yet central location of the den.

AREA: Upper level: 1,188 sq. ft.
Lower level: 773 sq. ft.
Garage: 415 sq. ft.

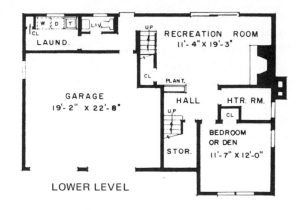

LOWER LEVEL

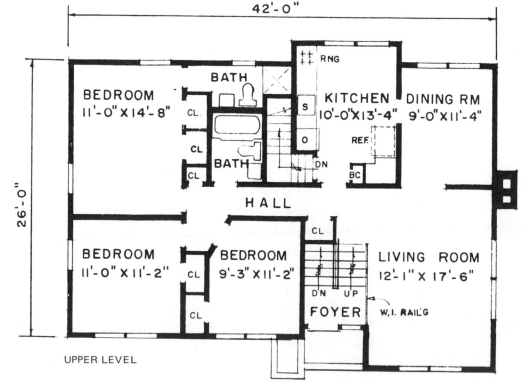

UPPER LEVEL

The Carlyle

Three large bedrooms and bath-dressing area for the master bedroom provide the privacy and roominess desired by any family. The large kitchen and dinette with adjacent dining room complement the airy living room highlighted by its stone planter.

Downstairs, the recreation room, with corner fireplace, bar, and kitchenette, provide an excellent opportunity for entertaining or just family fun. The spare room with lavatory is perfect as a den or for overnight guests.

AREA: Upper level: 1,266 sq. ft.
Lower level: 750 sq. ft.
Garage: 460 sq. ft.

LOWER LEVEL

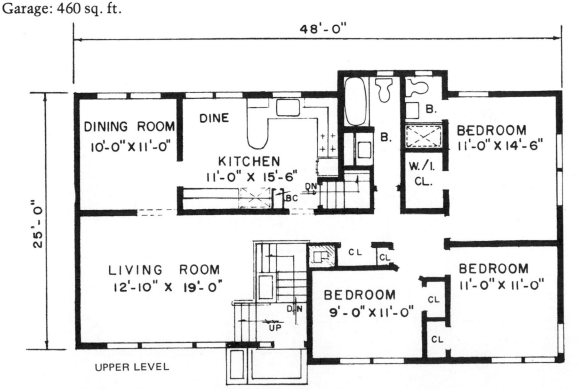

UPPER LEVEL

The Pendrey

This attractive bi-level will stand out in any neighborhood. Stepping through the striking entry, we find comfortable living in the cathedral-ceiling living room, dining room, and kitchen-dinette area. A private hall leads to three roomy bedrooms and two baths.

On the lower level, this livable plan is completed by the huge recreation room with fireplace and sliding glass door, study, lavatory, heater-laundry room, and two-car garage.

AREA: Upper level: 1,475 sq. ft.
    Lower level: 772 sq. ft.
    Garage: 703 sq. ft.

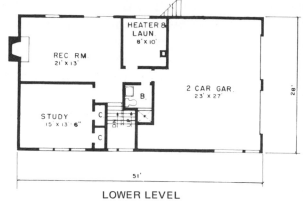

LOWER LEVEL

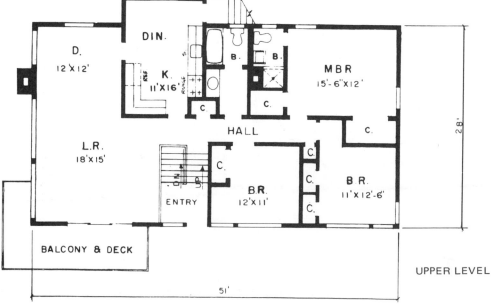

UPPER LEVEL

The Kingston

The basic living area of this home is all on one floor, "ranch style." The unusual feature of the split-entrance vestibule creates an exterior appearance of the formal, two-story colonial. This entrance feature also makes available the entire basement area for finishing liveable rooms.

Ranch homes are normally the most expensive to build per square foot of living area, but this ingenious arrangement of entrance tends to put this home nearer the category of two-story homes for economy of construction based on the total square feet of living area.

AREA: Upper level: 1,650 sq. ft.
Lower level: 600 sq. ft.

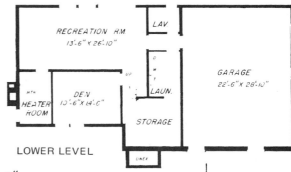

LOWER LEVEL

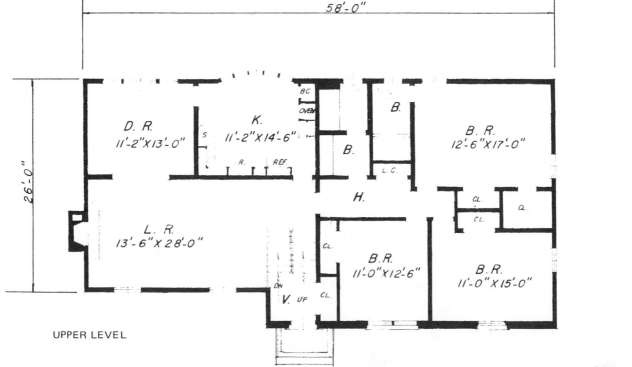

UPPER LEVEL

The Gateway

All the charm and elegance of the South are embodied in this traditional Southern colonial, three-bedroom, bi-level design with its two-story central portico, massive square pillars, and combination of brick veneer and red cedar shingle exterior.

Because of the economics of space utilization and construction, increasing numbers of today's home buyers are finding the "raised-ranch" to their liking for comfortable living, where routine family activity centers on the upper level, while the lower level is a spacious asset for entertaining and relaxation.

AREA: **Upper level:** 1,430 sq. ft.
Lower level: 880 sq. ft.
Garage: 550 sq. ft.

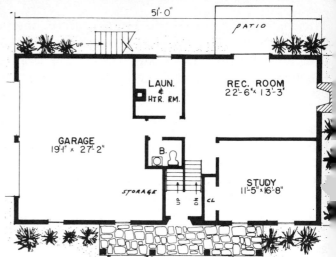

LOWER LEVEL

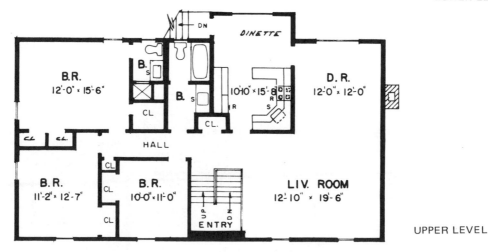

UPPER LEVEL

The Vanderbilt

This design, which retains all the romantic charm of the old English Tudor, is a typical "raised-ranch" plan with a complete, three bedroom, one-floor living unit set on top of a daylight basement which offers extra living space.

The traditional styling of the exterior is enhanced by the wood shingles, stucco, boxed living room bay, hand-hewn timber, and small-paned windows.

Inside, the family will find comfortable living in the spacious living room-dining room area and the efficient kitchen-dinette. The bedroom area has three bedrooms and two full baths, one private.

On the lower level, a recreation room and study add valuable living space; a lavatory, laundry, and two-car garage complete this well-designed plan.

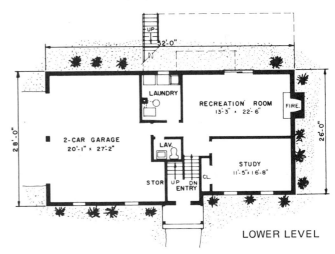

AREA: Upper level: 1,458 sq. ft.
Lower level, living area: 956 sq. ft.
Garage: 462 sq. ft.

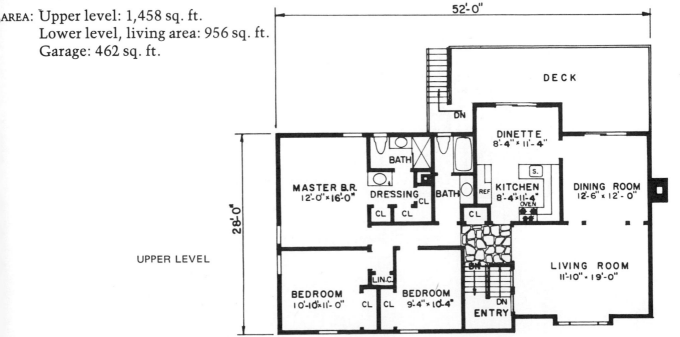

The Webster

One of today's most popular building types, the split-entry design is a fairly recent architectural approach to residential housing. Basically, it is a one-story house "raised" out of the ground about halfway.

The gracious exterior of this bi-level design will stand out in any neighborhood.

The well-designed interior will provide comfortable living for even the most demanding, active family.

AREA: **Upper level:** 1,555 sq. ft.
Lower level: 1,005 sq. ft.

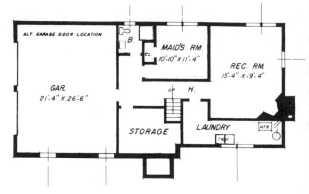

LOWER LEVEL

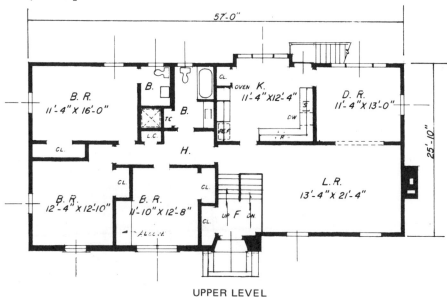

UPPER LEVEL

The Osborne

This intricate, three-level, ''raised-ranch'' plan produces an unusually good traffic pattern. The entrance foyer acts as a distribution point, up to the living and sleeping area, and down to the lower level, which features a recreation room with fireplace, a maid's room or den with bath, and a two-car garage.

Vertical lines and window treatments are emphasized on the dramatic exterior and enhanced by the floating wood deck, which provides outdoor living and dining off the kitchen-dinette.

The three bedrooms are well and conveniently serviced by the two baths and are supplied with ample closet space.

AREA: Upper level: 1,978 sq. ft.
      Lower level: 1,358 sq. ft.

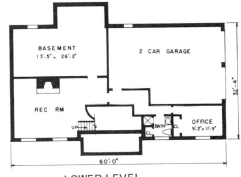

LOWER LEVEL

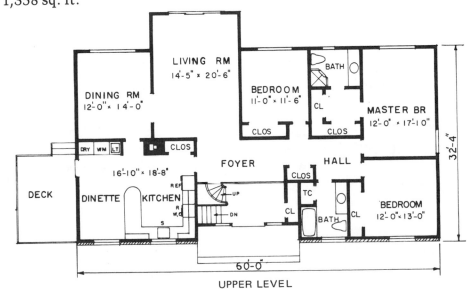

UPPER LEVEL

The Tiffany

Spaciousness and livability characterize this distinctive, mansard-type, multi-level design. Through the glass-framed main entrance, traffic is channeled to the upper and lower areas of the house. Two bedrooms and a palatial master bedroom suite with private bath are clustered together.

Both living and family rooms have direct access to the view-capturing rear deck, and the lower level features a recreation room, den, laundry, and complete bath.

AREA: Upper level: 2,565 sq. ft.
Lower level: 1,275 sq. ft.
Garage: 806 sq. ft.
Deck: 487 sq. ft.

LOWER LEVEL

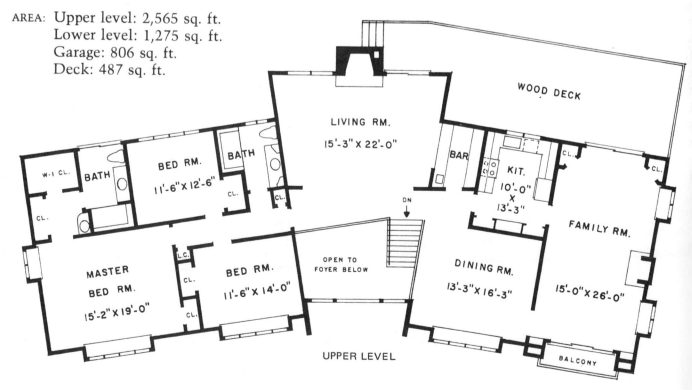

UPPER LEVEL

DOME HOMES

Because the factory-assembled, triangular space frames are simply bolted together on the site to form the finished building, a dome home can cost as much as 20 percent less than conventional housing. The dome provides maximum enclosed space with minimum surface area, which means efficiency in terms of heat-gain or heat-loss. It has been estimated that heating, cooling, and insurance costs can be reduced by at least 30 percent.

The Futura

This prefabricated, standard shell dome home is sold in "kit" form geared to "do-it-yourselfers." It can be easily assembled by one or two persons in a few days with ordinary household tools. The dome can be set on a ground-level concrete slabs or on wood floor beams if a full basement or crawl space construction is desired. Because the shell is self-supporting, you can subdivide the interior space any way you like.

Whether you are considering a vacation home, leisure-time second home, or a retreat in the mountains, this 26-foot-diameter model, with its soaring interior, offers a visual panorama. The skylights capture all of the sun's rays during the day and the stars at night.

AREA: 485 sq. ft.

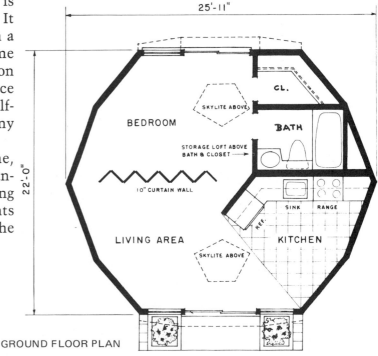

25'-11"

22'-0"

BEDROOM

CL.

SKYLITE ABOVE

BATH

STORAGE LOFT ABOVE
BATH & CLOSET →

10" CURTAIN WALL

SINK   RANGE

REF.

LIVING AREA

SKYLITE ABOVE

KITCHEN

GROUND FLOOR PLAN

The Leisure-Dome

If you have never been inside a dome home, you are in for a real surprise.

In this design, the dominant exterior architectural feature is the butterfly-roofed porte-cochere screened by the decorative fieldstone wall and water fountains. The most dramatic space inside the home is the panoramic living-dining-balcony space topped off by gigantic pentagon skylights.

A decorative metal circular staircase provides ready access to the upper level.

AREA: Ground floor: 1,135 sq. ft.
Loft: 385 sq. ft.
Storage area: 56 sq. ft.

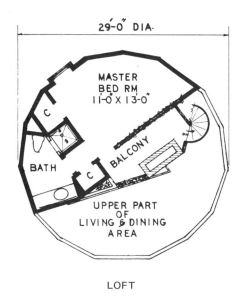

LOFT

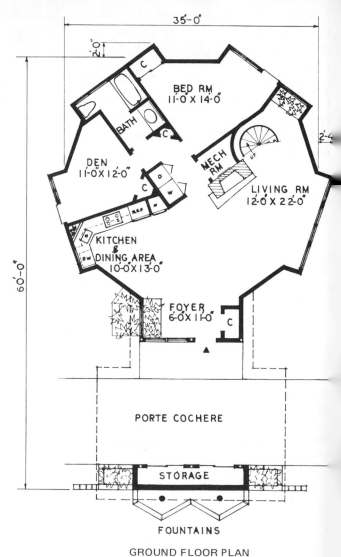

GROUND FLOOR PLAN

The Pentagon

This design in today's "dome homes" is among the best in efficient and economical housing. With the den, which can be used as an alternate second bedroom, the step-saver kitchen, full bath, and spacious living-dining area, you have all the space you need for a year-round residence, a vacation home in the mountains, on a lake, or at the ocean. If you desire, the second level may be omitted to save construction costs and increase the marvelous feeling of dome space living.

AREA: Ground floor: 1,085 sq. ft.
Loft: 380 sq. ft.

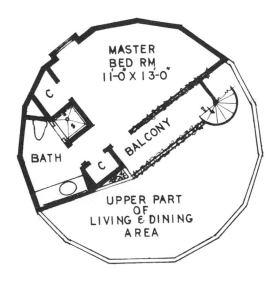

LOFT

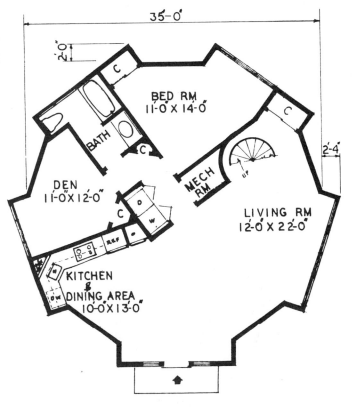

GROUND FLOOR PLAN

A House Planning Guide From A to Z

A   After you have chosen your building site, obtain the services of a land surveyor to provide you with a topographical survey of your property. The survey should include grade contours, lot lines (their direction and length), location and depth of sewers (if available), water main, gas, electric, etc. All easements, existing trees and other physical characteristics should be clearly indicated.

B   Before beginning preliminary sketches, it is recommended that copies of all rules and regulations governing the building activity of your area be obtained. This includes a local building code, local zoning restrictions, fire underwriters' regulations, local, city, or state sanitary requirements, etc.

C   Committing yourself to a construction contract for the erection of your home is a matter of great and serious concern. If you do not have the cash necessary to pay for the entire construction cost, a building loan will be needed. A building loan or mortgage may be obtained from your local bank, building loan companies, savings and loan associations, insurance companies, mortgage firms or private individuals. A long-term amortizing mortgage with monthly installments arranged like rent is the most convenient. These installments include interest, insurance, payment on principal, and frequently, taxes and water.

D   Design your house to be in harmony with those in the neighborhood. Strive for architectural appeal by simple lines which will lend dignity to the structure. A well-designed house gets a high mortgage rating.

E   Economy in placing one bath over or adjacent to another is desirable, but this calls for discretion. An apparent saving of $100 in plumbing costs might be more than offset by square foot loss and inconvenience to the occupants.

F   For an accurate estimate of the cost of your home, submit your plans and specifications to a builder or contractor. Cost per square foot is a good "rule of thumb" figure but may vary depending on special built-in features, building codes, etc.

G   Good residential design requires sound imagination, thought, originality, and experience which can only be obtained from an architect. If you intend to use stock plans to construct your home, be sure they are the work of an architect, not a designer.

H   Have the title searched on your property. This will protect you as the owner. When the title has been cleared, you will get a deed which should be recorded in the proper court.

I   If you wish to maintain the value of your property through the years, select a lot where the zoning ordinances have been established. They will protect your property against the encroachments of business, rooming houses, multi-family dwellings, and other adverse influences.

J   Just build a home to meet your immediate needs; don't go for too big a house. Don't expect to get all your ideas in one house but decide on a plan that is a compromise.

K   Keep an open mind on new materials and methods. Consider building in several stages: what you need, build now; what you might need, build later.

L   Land is scarce and getting more so every day. You will pay more for land today than it cost several years ago and chances are that it will cost more in the future. When you have decided on the lot, make sure you obtain an owner's title insurance policy.

M Modern residential building construction is a complicated job in which scheduling of the work of various sub-contractors is very important. Masons, plumbers, electricians, plasterers, tile setters, carpenters, etc., must be coordinated with each other to avoid time consuming, costly delays.

N Neighborhoods should have houses of different styles and prices. Stay clear from areas which seem to have all the houses built from the same basic design.

O Once you have determined your own particular home requirements—two, three, or four bedrooms—the only other cost factors are the size of the house in square feet, number of baths and lavatories and the amount of livability per square foot.

P Plan your house to fit the lot and avoid the costly need of changing the existing topography to fit the house.

Q Quite apart from the topography of your individual lot, you should note the terrain of the surrounding land. Proper drainage of your lot, as well as the adjacent property, is of utmost importance.

R Recommendations on good building contractors should be obtained from your architect, lawyer, real estate broker, lumber dealer, building supply house, bank or other lending institutions. Ask these builders for a list of the houses they have recently completed. It may be worth your while to visit and talk with some of the people whose homes they built.

S Select a local reputable contractor or builder, and make only written agreements in order to avoid future misunderstandings.

T Trick designs adversely affect the value of your property. It is unwise to build a home that is radically different in an "established" neighborhood.

U Unless you have unlimited funds and can afford to experiment and make mistakes, do not accept radical architectural designs or untried new materials and mechanical equipment. Unless you have a background in the building field, don't count on saving money by trying to act as your own general contractor.

V Visit your lot several times on different days and under different weather conditions. Carefully check the surrounding neighborhood and the orientation of the lot. A pleasant view adds to the enjoyment of life; a viewless lot, however, can be greatly improved by anyone with a talent for landscaping and gardening.

W When you apply for a loan, the bank or other lending institution will want to know exactly where and what you intend to build. Bring along a copy of your house plans and specifications, a plot plan and a legal description of your property. Be sure you are prepared to establish your financial responsibility.

X Extraordinary precautions should be exercised in establishing your cost limitations. Your home may represent THE largest investment you will make in your lifetime. There is no substitute for good planning, good materials, good workmanship, and safe and sound financing.

Y Your first step in building your home should be to consult a lawyer. His fee is moderate and his services, priceless. Explain your proposed building program to him. He will advise you about local procedures and will protect you from making costly mistakes every time you sign your name to a contract agreement.

Z Zoning regulations control what you can build on your lot. They are a definite protection for the homeowner, because they keep commercial and industrial business out of residential areas and thus tend to maintain real estate and property values.

Which House For You?
Construction Costs,
And Mortgage Financing

Once you have determined your requirements and made up your mind to build your new home, further decisions will be much easier to make if you familiarize yourself with the type or design, personal preference, and budget patterns. Whether the design you select is a ranch, split-level, or two-story, you should not confuse the architectural with the descriptive title such as colonial, French, Tudor, farmhouse, etc. which may be adapted to any house.

The debate is never-ending on the relative merits of ranch, split-level, and two-story homes. Evidence can be marshalled by advocates of each style that their favorite is best for all-around economy, livability, and other virtues.

Rectangular perimeters offer the least expensive base construction, and simple straight roof lines, the most economical cover for the base. Given a fixed area and price, the least expensive is a small rectangular one-story building; a two-story house with the same size foundation and roof would give double the living area, but at less than double the cost. A split-level of the same original foundation size would increase the living area over the one-story. This is usually accomplished by "lifting" the bedroom area so that the basement floor below comes up to grade level, thereby providing additional living space on-grade in cellar space which had been previously below ground. This "lifting" process causes some extra expense in framing and roofing, but provides the extra living area at less cost than it would take to obtain this area in the original one-story building by making a larger foundation area and shaping the ranch into the familiar, rambling "L," "U," or "T" shape.

The debate cannot be resolved on construction cost alone. There are other features desirable and important in the arrangement of the plan to afford comfortable and convenient living. One point on which all agree: there should be definite separation between living, sleeping, and recreation areas. Here also a controversy arises—should this separation be horizontal or vertical? The ranch house can effectively provide this separation by proper planning of the interior layout. This is more difficult with the simple, basic rectangle—hence the rambling design usually present in the ranch. It is simple to design a bedroom wing and a recreation wing if they can extend in any direction away from the central core of living area. When stairs are no objection, the two-story layout provides this separation quite definitely and most satisfactorily. In the split-level or other multi-level arrangements, there are usually 3 basic living levels. Each is separated by a short flight of stairs, thereby carrying to a finer degree the separation between living, sleeping, and recreation areas by providing a separate level for each.

In this modern age the sleek, streamlined look seems most appealing to many people even though they strive to obtain the character of detail inherent in the old colonial architecture. The two-story house would have to be large to obtain this effect, and generally would have a stately, rather than streamlined, appearance. The ranch or one-story home can have this pleasing effect even though small. If it is larger and is designed in some shape other than rectangular, the "rambling ranch" appearance is very attractive.

Split-levels are highly adaptable to many styles of exterior appearance. Ingenious arrangements of roof line and adjustments of levels can give two-story as well as ranch-like character to the conventional split-level home. The front-to-back and back-to-front split-levels can strongly suggest a ranch-type home and a two-story home, respectively. Purely for its own style, the conventional split-level suggests a house of separate wings, each for its own specific use. This is generally considered to be a sign of an expensive home.

Economy in heating and plumbing is another feature strongly debated by advocates of the different types of homes. The lower level recreation area of the split-level has long been a thorn in the side when it comes to proper heat. The introduction of the 2-zone system has eliminated this to some extent when using forced warm air. The usual concrete slab floor construction here has some advantages when using hot water heat, however. The installation of hot water piping in this concrete and the resultant warm floor and radiant heat provide the most comfortable area in the house in the winter.

Of course, proper insulation is the best controlling factor for economy of operation in any heating system. It will protect a bedroom floor when it is located over an unheated garage or a wall of a room located next to a garage. Naturally, exterior walls and ceilings at unheated attic areas are "must" locations for insulation. Most economical plumbing arrangements concentrate in one small area those rooms which require plumbing. Small homes have baths located next to the kitchen with a result of less separation between sleeping and living areas. Ingenious hall arrangement can overcome this proximity somewhat, but for complete separation in the ranch plan, separate plumbing areas can be expected to increase costs.

Home Financing:

Owning your own home has been greatly simplified during the past thirty years. The modern long-term, low-interest, self-amortizing mortgage (covering principal, interest, taxes, and insurance) has changed the whole institution of home buying. Under this plan the prospective homeowner makes regular monthly payments on the money that is borrowed. The real estate taxes and the interest you pay on your home are tax deductible.

There are basically three different types of mortgage loans: conventional, VA, and FHA (U.S. Housing & Urban Development).

Conventional loans are usually obtained through the banks and other institutions. Since there is only so much money to lend these days, these institutions are trying to make the best of the situation by getting more and more selective, at interest rates higher than for FHA or VA loans.

National, state, and mutual savings banks, building and loan associations, insurance companies, and mortgage bankers represent the major mortgage lending agencies. In the long run, most people find dealing with their own local bank or institution far more satisfactory than dealing with an agent representing other institutions.

The Federal Housing Administration (HUD) does not make mortgage loans. Instead, it insures the mortgage loans made through some 30,000 lending agencies. This protection enables lending institu-

tions to make insured mortgage loans on desirable terms, with a small down payment and government-limited financing rates.

The Veterans Administration also guarantees GI loans through regular lending institutions. If you are an ex-serviceman or woman, you may qualify for a lower down payment and a longer-term mortgage than civilians who have not served in the armed forces.

From time to time the government varies both the percentage of down payments required, the maximum number of years the mortgage may run, and the prevailing interest rate. Check with your local lending institution to see what rates are current before you start.

Construction Costs:

There are several methods of estimating the approximate costs of any new home. The one most used by architects, builders, and appraisers is the square foot method. Geographic locations vary the cost of both materials and labor. Local building conditions and codes differ to such a wide degree than an accurate unit scale is almost impractical. Generally speaking, constructions costs range upward from $25 a square foot of living area, assuming that the work is contracted out to a contractor. Any work that you may do yourself, such as painting, decorating, landscaping, etc., would reduce the cost.

Remember that only your builder can give you an exact and final building cost figure, and that the "rule of thumb" yardstick, as outlined above, is merely for your generalized, "fireside" consultation. By multiplying the square foot area by the construction estimate, you will be able to catalogue the design that interests you most into a general price category. (The cost of land, of course, will be entirely separate.)

Selecting a Builder:

To build the home you have selected requires the services of a reliable contractor. Recommendations may come from friends who have built or are building a new home, or perhaps you can obtain the names of the contractors who may be constructing homes in the newly-developed areas of your town.

If you know someone who had a home built and was satisfied with the result, ask for the name of the contractor.

Since you will definitely want to obtain several bids, interview several contractors, and, if possible, visit some of the homes that they have built during the last few years.

Many builders belong to the National Association of Home Builders. Although the NAHB is a national organization which officially credits home builders with a certain level of professionalism, a small builder (one who builds only two or three houses a year) may not belong, but still be competent and reliable.

Finally, do not sign any papers or agreements without the presence of a lawyer, whose services can help you avoid extremely costly mistakes in dealing with the builder, title company, or money lending institution.

How to Build Your Home

Your first step in building your home should be to consult a local lawyer. His fee will be moderate and his services, priceless.

Both husband and wife should attend when the lawyer is involved in discussions and paper signing.

Explain your proposed building program to him. He will advise you about local procedures; he will protect you from making costly mistakes, and he will be on hand every time you sign your name to a contract or agreement.

Buy Property

In most cases, you will be unable to obtain mortgage financing without ownership of the property on which your house is to be built. So this is the next step.

When you have found a lot which meets all your requirements, call in your lawyer. He will determine whether you really will be the owner of the land you are ready to pay for. The seller must be able to furnish you with a "clear title." Your lawyer will advise you how to proceed on this.

While this title search is going on, a prudent way to protect your interests is to have the deal held in escrow. That means turning the purchase price over to a third party (your own or the seller's lawyer, the real estate broker, your bank, or the title company) until the title is cleared. Once the deal is in escrow, you can proceed with the plot survey. Engage a local surveyor or civil engineer, because he probably has done other work in the neighborhood and may have time-saving data on file in his office, which will be reflected in his fee.

A complete plot survey shows on paper every outline, every angle, every dimension of your plot. The location, size, and depth of underground sewers, water mains, and gas lines should be plotted with the house connection stubs, if any. The survey should show the location of adjacent houses, if any, nearest your line on either side to permit placing your house to secure maximum privacy, light, and prevailing breezes.

A plot survey includes permanent markers on the ground on every corner and at every angle if the plot is irregular.

While your title is being searched, arrange to take out a title guarantee policy. It usually is cheaper to get an owner's title insurance policy from the company making the title search in connection with the sale. This is because the search and examination will not have to be duplicated, and the cost of this loss-prevention work on the part of the company accounts for the bulk of the title policy charge.

The biggest advantage to you in title insurance is that the title company must defend any claim made against your ownership. The cost of such a defense could exceed the cost of your whole home. The fact that the mortgage lender will also carry title insurance is not adequate for you; his covers the amount of the mortgage; your title insurance must also protect your equity over the amount of the mortgage.

When your title has been cleared, you will get a deed. Have this recorded in the proper court. You will pay a revenue stamp tax on the purchase price.

You have now acquired the site. It is protected against trouble. You are now ready to build your new home.

Arranging a Loan

Rarely do families have the amount of cash necessary to pay the entire construction cost of the home; you will probably need to borrow money to build. What you need is a building loan.

This building loan is usually converted automatically into a mortgage when the house is completed. Terms of the mortgage will be established when you arrange the building loan.

Usually a builder will not start work without some down payment and an agreement on a schedule of payments to be made at regular intervals during the course of construction. Find out the financial requirements of the builder you select and establish whether he is to be paid directly by you or the lending institution. Your lawyer will help you. As a guide for your reference, here is a typical schedule of payments to the contractor while the house is being built:

10% on completion of foundation
25% on completion of the rough enclosure
30% on completion of the plastering, plumbing, heating, and electricity
25% on completion of the work
10% 30 days after completion of all work

Withholding of the final payment for 30 days is to insure correction of any defects or oversights. This should be mentioned specifically in your agreement with the builder which your lawyer will draw up for you.

At the time each payment is made to the builder, have your lawyer make certain that it is in accord with the original agreement and that you receive a proper statement of receipt. Before the final payment is made, your lawyer should carefully verify that there are no liens or outstanding unpaid bills that might become a claim against you.

You can get your building loan and mortgage money from banks, local building and loan companies, or mortgage firms.

These lending institutions are in business to make money and they have just one commodity for sale—money. There is real competition among lending agencies for your business. Do not hesitate to shop around for terms.

Talk to a number of these representatives, but do not make out a formal application for a loan until you have studied their offers. Most home-owners find the long-term mortgage, with monthly installments arranged like rent, the most convenient. These installments include interest, insurance, payment on principal and, frequently, tax and water charges.

Interest rates vary. A fraction of 1% saved each year amounts to a sizable sum over the term of your mortgage. Depending on conditions in the money market, rates vary. Even though you may not need the biggest loan you can get, it is reassuring to know you could raise more funds.

Check to see how much the cost will be, if at some later time you might wish to pay off your mortgage because of a gift or inheritance, and after what period you can repay without penalty.

When you apply for a loan, the bank or other lending institution will want to know exactly where and what you intend to build. Be sure you take with you a copy of the house plans and specifications, and plot plan or short legal description of the property.

You must be prepared to establish your financial responsibility as a good risk. This means a statement of your assets and liabilities, income and employment record. A good "rule of thumb" is that 20% to 25% of your yearly gross income should equal or exceed your yearly payments on principal, interest, taxes, insurance, and maintenance of your home.

Here are some questions from a typical loan application form: what is your employment record, position held, salary, number of years on the job, previous positions with other firms, bank accounts, life insurance and amount of annual premiums, previous mortgage experience, stocks and securities held, other income, number of dependents, judgments or garnishments against your salary?

Building Permit

A building permit is generally required before construction is started. Your builder may handle this for you or you may apply for it through your local building department. Two sets of house and plot plans are usually sufficient to submit with the application. One set will be returned with the building permit. A small fee is generally charged for the building permit.

MORTGAGE PAYMENT TABLE

Amounts shown include monthly payments of interest and principal but not taxes and insurance.

20-YEAR MORTGAGE

Amount	at 8½%	at 9%	at 9½%	at 10%	at 10½%	at 11%	at 11½%	at 12%
$16,000	137.68	144.00	149.15	154.41	159.75	165.16	170.63	176.18
20,000	173.60	180.00	186.43	193.01	199.68	206.44	213.29	220.22
24,000	208.32	216.00	223.72	231.61	239.62	247.73	254.95	264.27
28,000	243.04	252.00	261.00	270.21	279.55	289.02	298.61	308.31
30,000	260.40	270.00	279.64	289.51	299.52	309.66	319.93	330.33
36,000	312.48	324.00	335.57	347.41	359.42	371.60	383.93	396.41
40,000	347.20	360.00	372.86	386.01	399.36	412.88	426.59	440.44
44,000	381.92	396.00	410.14	424.61	439.29	454.17	469.24	484.49
50,000	434.00	450.00	466.07	482.52	499.19	516.10	533.22	550.55
54,000	468.72	486.00	503.36	521.12	539.13	557.39	543.89	594.60
60,000	520.80	540.00	559.28	579.02	599.03	619.32	639.86	660.66
64,000	555.52	576.00	596.57	617.62	638.97	660.61	682.52	704.61

25-YEAR MORTGAGE

Amount	at 8½%	at 9%	at 9½%	at 10%	at 10½%	at 11%	at 11½%	at 12%
$16,000	128.84	134.27	139.80	145.40	151.07	156.82	162.34	168.52
20,000	161.05	167.84	174.74	181.75	188.84	196.03	203.30	210.65
24,000	193.25	201.41	209.69	218.09	226.61	235.23	243.96	252.78
28,000	225.46	234.97	244.64	254.44	264.38	274.44	284.62	294.91
30,000	241.57	251.76	262.11	272.62	283.26	294.04	304.95	315.97
36,000	289.88	302.11	314.54	327.14	339.91	352.85	365.94	379.17
40,000	322.09	335.68	349.48	363.49	377.68	392.05	406.59	421.29
44,000	354.30	369.25	384.43	399.83	415.44	431.26	447.25	462.54
50,000	402.61	419.60	436.85	454.36	472.10	490.06	508.24	526.62
54,000	434.82	453.17	471.80	490.70	509.86	529.27	518.41	568.75
60,000	483.14	503.52	524.22	545.23	566.51	588.07	609.89	631.94
64,000	515.35	537.09	559.17	581.57	604.28	627.28	650.55	674.07

Is Now The *Time* to Build?

Perhaps you are asking yourself such questions as: Are we ready to build now? Can we go ahead this year? Or will next year be better?

For most families facing this decision, the best answer is to do it *now*. Due to our recent inflationary economy, the value of homes has doubled or tripled during the past twenty years, so the odds are that, due to economic realities, homes will continue to increase in value because of the expected rise in labor and the cost of materials. Any long-term investment like a home must rise in value during an inflationary economy. If you postpone the construction of your new home for even as short a time as one year, you may well find that the cost will have risen by as much as ten percent.

More importantly, the decision to go ahead now will enable your family that much sooner to start enjoying the better living and the enhanced security that your new home will provide. Just as building costs rise, so do the total dollar values of homes; you can safely expect the home you build this year to be worth several thousand dollars more than its cost ten years from now. In the meantime, as a homeowner, you will be enjoying special income tax advantages in the fact that your payments for mortgage interest and real estate taxes are fully deductible. Finally, your payments of mortgage principal will each month decrease the amount you owe; by meeting your monthly payments, your equity grows as automatically as if you were making regular deposits in a savings account.

So, for an investment whose value and equity grows, and the psychological motivation of owning your own home, the time to proceed with arrangements for the construction of your new home is now.

About Your Home . . .
Before You Write—Read!

We welcome correspondence and are happy to answer your letters,
but why not save yourself time and effort?
Perhaps the answer to your question is here.

Are cost estimates included or can you tell me how much my favorite house will cost to build?

• Construction costs vary so much from one section of the country to another that you will do better to get a set of blueprints of your favorite plan and obtain an estimate locally. Costs range upwards from $25 a square foot of living space, assuming that the work is contracted out. Our designs show the square feet of living area. Unless otherwise specified, this does not include porches, terraces, garages, etc., since many of these features are optional and, of course, cost less per square foot to build than the main dwelling. With our blueprints you can get actual local cost estimates from builders and arrange financing with a mortgage lending institution.

Will you make plan changes for us?

• In most instances, changes in dimensions, substitution of items, materials, etc., or minor alterations can be done by the contractor during construction. If the house plan calls for wood siding, it can be changed to brick, stone or other materials; only the width of the exterior walls must be adjusted for the difference. We furnish conversion details, otherwise the working drawings for our designs are available only as illustrated. If major changes are involved, you should consider ordering one set of blueprints and having them redrawn by your local architect.

Will you tell me where a particular house has been built so I can look at it?

• During the past twenty years, we have sold many thousands of our plans for homes that have been built throughout the entire country. Unfortunately, our blueprint buyers seldom give us any information as to where or when they expect to build. Our design illustrations are accurately drawn perspectives and, with the exception of the landscaping, the house will appear exactly as shown.

Will plans meet local building codes?

• Our plans have been engineered for sound construction, but as long as there are almost as many different building codes as there are communities, there are bound to be rare cases of conflict. There is no need for concern, however, inasmuch as any suggested changes can usually be done during construction without the necessity of new or revised plans.

Can I get blueprints "in reverse" with the living room, for instance, on the left instead of the right as shown?

• If you find that your favorite house plan would suit you—or your lot—better if it were reversed, we will, upon request, send one of the sets transposed as in a mirror. Even though the lettering and dimensions appear backward, they make a handy reference because they show the house just as it's being built in reverse from the standard blueprints—thereby helping you visualize the home better. For example, if you order five sets of plans, we will send one mirror image, and four in the original position so that you can read the figures and directions easily.

How many sets of blueprints should be ordered?

• The answer can range anywhere from one to eight sets depending upon circumstances. A single set of blueprints of your favorite design is sufficient to study the house in greater detail. If you desire to get cost estimates, or are planning to build, you may need as many as eight sets of blueprints. For building, a minimum of five sets is required, one each for: owner, builder, material dealer, building permit, and mortgage financing. In many cases, local building departments require two complete sets of blueprints before they will issue a building permit. (Check with your local building department.) You may need six sets.

How is the low cost of your blueprints possible?

• If you had complete working drawings especially

created by a personal architect, the design fee for an individual home could be eight to ten percent of the total construction cost, and could range from several hundred dollars up to several thousand, depending on how big and complicated the design is. When you use our architect-designed plans (prepared by and/or under the supervision of professional licensed architects), the cost is spread among other families planning to build the same house in various parts of the country and they are sharing the total costs with you. Our many years of practical home planning experience assure you of a well-designed, practical house which will stay younger longer and make you feel proud of owning the home of your dreams.

Do you furnish a description of materials or material list?

• All of our working drawings are furnished with a suggested description of materials required to construct the house as illustrated. Many contractors and material dealers prefer, however, to make up their own material list to take full advantage of materials most readily obtainable at best prices locally, thus permitting the substitution of items to satisfy your personal preference.

Plan Orders Mailed Within 24 Hours!

HOW TO ORDER YOUR BLUEPRINTS!

If the design you have selected satisfies your requirements, mail the accompanying order blank with your remittance. However, if it is not convenient for you to send a check or money order, merely indicate C.O.D. shipment.

We will make every effort to process and ship each order for blueprints the same day it is received. Because of this, we have deemed it unnecessary to acknowledge receipt of our customers' orders. See order coupon below for the postage and handling charges for surface mail, air mail, and foreign mail.

Should time be of the essence, as it sometimes is—
For Immediate Service
Phone (201) 376–3200
Your plans will be shipped C.O.D. Postman will collect all charges, including postage. (No C.O.D. shipments to Canada or foreign countries.)

NATIONAL HOME PLANNING SERVICE
37 Mountain Avenue
Springfield, N.J. 07081   Phone Orders (201) 376-3200

PLEASE SEND HOME DESIGN, BUILDING PLAN NAME: THE _____

First set of Plans (if only one is desired)	$ 85.00	$_____
Each additional set with original order .... @	$ 20.00	$_____
To have Plans Reversed	$ 10.00	$_____
Five (5) sets of Architect's Total Blueprint and Building Package	$125.00	$_____

ADD THE FOLLOWING POSTAGE:

Parcel Post (allow 2 to 3 weeks)	$ 4.00	$_____
First Class-Air Mail	$ 5.00	$_____
C O D (U S Only)	$ 6.00	$_____
Canada and Foreign Air Mail	$10.00	$_____
Make payment in U.S. currency to National Home Planning Service	TOTAL AMOUNT	$_____

Prices subject to change without notice!

MAIL ORDER TO:
NAME _____
STREET _____
CITY _____ STATE _____ ZIP _____

NATIONAL HOME PLANNING SERVICE

37 Mountain Avenue

Springfield, N.J. 07081   Phone Orders (201) 376-3200

PLEASE SEND HOME DESIGN, BUILDING PLAN NAME — THE _____

First set of Plans (if only one is desired)		$ 85.00	$_____
Each additional set with original order	@	$ 20.00	$_____
To have Plans Reversed		$ 10.00	$_____
Five (5) sets of Architect's Total Blueprint and Building Package		$125.00	$_____

ADD THE FOLLOWING POSTAGE:

Parcel Post (allow 2 to 3 weeks)	$ 4.00	$_____
First Class-Air Mail	$ 5.00	$_____
C.O.D. (U.S. Only)	$ 6.00	$_____
Canada and Foreign Air Mail	$10.00	$_____
Make payment in U.S. currency to National Home Planning Service	TOTAL AMOUNT	$_____

Prices subject to change without notice!

MAIL ORDER TO:

NAME: _____

STREET: _____

CITY: _____ STATE: _____ ZIP: _____

FMC-2

NATIONAL HOME PLANNING SERVICE

37 Mountain Avenue

Springfield, N.J. 07081   Phone Orders (201) 376-3200

PLEASE SEND HOME DESIGN, BUILDING PLAN NAME — THE _____

First set of Plans (if only one is desired)		$ 85.00	$_____
Each additional set with original order	@	$ 20.00	$_____
To have Plans Reversed		$ 10.00	$_____
Five (5) sets of Architect's Total Blueprint and Building Package		$125.00	$_____

ADD THE FOLLOWING POSTAGE:

Parcel Post (allow 2 to 3 weeks)	$ 4.00	$_____
First Class-Air Mail	$ 5.00	$_____
C.O.D. (U.S. Only)	$ 6.00	$_____
Canada and Foreign Air Mail	$10.00	$_____
Make payment in U.S. currency to National Home Planning Service	TOTAL AMOUNT	$_____

Prices subject to change without notice!

MAIL ORDER TO:

NAME: _____

STREET: _____

CITY: _____ STATE: _____ ZIP: _____

FMC-2

NATIONAL HOME PLANNING SERVICE

37 Mountain Avenue

Springfield, N.J. 07081   Phone Orders (201) 376-3200

PLEASE SEND HOME DESIGN, BUILDING PLAN NAME — THE _____

First set of Plans (if only one is desired)		$ 85.00	$_____
Each additional set with original order	@	$ 20.00	$_____
To have Plans Reversed		$ 10.00	$_____
Five (5) sets of Architect's Total Blueprint and Building Package		$125.00	$_____

ADD THE FOLLOWING POSTAGE:

Parcel Post (allow 2 to 3 weeks)	$ 4.00	$_____
First Class-Air Mail	$ 5.00	$_____
C.O.D. (U.S. Only)	$ 6.00	$_____
Canada and Foreign Air Mail	$10.00	$_____
Make payment in U.S. currency to National Home Planning Service	TOTAL AMOUNT	$_____

Prices subject to change without notice!

MAIL ORDER TO:

NAME: _____

STREET: _____

CITY: _____ STATE: _____ ZIP: _____

FMC-2